TERROR STRIKES

TERROR STRIKES

COMING SOON TO A CITY NEAR YOU

JOSEPH M. LENARD

TERROR STRIKES

Published by
McHenry Press

Library of Congress Control Number: 2022904094

Paperback ISBN: 978-1-955043-66-3

Typeset by Art Innovations
Cover design by Debbie Lewis

Printed in the United States of America

CONTENTS

ACKNOWLEDGMENTS

Thank you to...

... all those who have suffered loss due to the cowardly attacks against the United States' innocent citizens that occurred throughout the years and especially September 11, 2001 – to which I said I would NEVER FORGET and I shall indeed Never Forget and I carry a tribute to you all on my right arm.

... Rhonda Michelle. I love you! Yes, I still have great fondness for you, and you have a permanent place in my heart. And, yes, I still think of you and pray for you.

... my mother (Donna Jean) who sadly passed July 2021 after many years of dealing with dementia (and while I would have loved to have had this book published prior to her passing, given her health and mental state would not have been able to appreciate the accomplishment anyway. I know; however, she will be looking down from heaven at this). My father (Thaddeus Martin) who sadly passed years before mom, in April 2013 (finally reunited with his bride in 2021). My sister (Michelle Collette), who is the rock or the lighthouse still guiding my life. Without my sister now, my life would be empty and meaningless. Their support over the years, decades, gave my life meaning and direction.

... my grandfather (Edward Kieler), from whom I have derived most of my life's guiding influence. As with the remainder of our extended family, whose care and love provided encouragement and reason culminating in some of the greatest aspects and underlying concepts I hope I conveyed successfully amongst the fictional precepts.

... "Mustang Lana" (wherever you may be now, as we've fallen out of touch years ago) for being a good sounding board for my ideas before they made it into the book. Thank you for our conversations which lead to inspirations, to new ideas, and the expansion of existing thoughts. I wish you could have been a part of this book's completion, now, finally, in 2022. Your enthusiasm was contagious and kept me driving forward toward this book's completion and release.

... all my friends and acquaintances along life's journey. You have all been a great sense of comfort and companionship for me as I hope that I have been or will be for each other going forward. Some of you are no longer in my life, rest assured you played a part in making me the person I have become, and I am grateful for you still being, or having been, a part of my life.

... all those of you who have so graciously chosen to spend some time with me through the advent of the pages of this publication. I hope that you find some of what you may be looking for within these printed sheets of paper. Whether you seek merely entertainment, enlightenment, or other goal.

... all the crew at ILLUMIFY MEDIA.

... first responders (Corrections, Dispatch, EMS/EMT, Fire, Law Enforcement, Military).

... those helping others through charitable pursuits (please help pay it forward - see: http://TerrorStrikes.info/charities).

And, of course, thoughts and prayers to family of so many of those we've lost. Rest in peace, your memory lives on in us all.

Ye are the light of the world. A city that is set on an hill cannot be hid. (Matthew 5:14)

DISCLAIMER

*A*ll names, characters, and incidents portrayed herein are of a completely fictitious nature or used fictitiously. No identification of any event(s) with actual person(s), living or dead; place(s); building(s); product(s); or organization(s); is intended or should be inferred.

Portions of this book contain dramatized versions of event(s) with special attention given to historical accuracy, with added dramatization of purely fictional origin.

Opinion(s) expressed here-in are provided for dramatization purposes only and may not reflect that of the author(s), publisher(s), and/or other parties/person(s) involved with the production or promotion of this publication. This work may contain colloquialisms and/or slang, as well as grammatical usage(s) and/or regional dialect implications, constructs purely the product of the author and out of traditional English language norms.

The use of product(s), location(s), and dramatized uses of service(s) or other potentially proprietary information here-in, are for dramatization purposes only and are at the sole discretion of the author(s)/creator(s) of this production. No consideration for use has been provided for portrayal.

This book is intended for all audiences - young, old, and everywhere in-between; male, female; religious, non-religious; political, non-political. However, it is impossible to address the topic and why they want to kill us without delving into some religious texts and politics. The Torah, the Holy Bible, and the Quran, are all addressed.

More information at: http://TerrorStrikes.info

SYNOPSIS

*G*ain an inside look into the terrorist tracks leading up to the deadliest attack on American soil as well as the existing real dangers still posed by those who wish to form American public opinion, and manipulate behavior through scare tactics, by targeting innocents.

When *Terror Strikes ... Terrorist Tracks*, the book within the book being developed by Marten, weaves a tale of factual events and fictional portrayal of a hypothetical scenario of a soon to take place attack on Americans in the heartland to send a message that no one is safe from the contended long reach of fanatic al Qaeda, ISIS, ISIL, and other Jihad-fundamentalists – a.k.a. GIJIAS (Global Islamic Jihad Interim Army Soldiers).

This is NOT a book about death, but one about LIFE (and living) and of those (foreign and domestic) that would deprive others of that Life, Liberty, and Pursuit of Happiness.

FROM THE BOOK . . . AWAKENING . . .

Marten realized the indefectible truth that the war against terrorism was the ultimate existential fight of good versus evil. It is the undeniable struggle of those who desire all mankind to live in peace and prosperity against those whose hate is based on jealousy, blind bigotry, unrestrained power, and unjustified and irrational religious notions.

Marten thought about how these GIJIA (Global Islamic Jihad Interim Army) or GIJIAS (Global Islamic Jihad Interim Army Soldiers) members, believers, and supporters, misguided by personal scars that foment hatred, desire for power, and vengeance, are driven to kill.

Misconceived and distorted notions of non-Islamic peoples provide a fertile ground to weave the deceptive seeds of hate. This perverse conjecture of lumping entire classes of people into one prejudiced assembly, of course, is not limited to today's terrorist hate mongers, but it has never before been such a prevalent and destructive force.

Marten knew that GIJIA consist of the most extreme Islamic/Muslim radicals, fundamentalists, and, as some would even point out correctly, fascists. It is quite clear that these individuals, and those that support them, believe that they are the only ones qualified to determine what is moral and good and that they must impose those beliefs on the world. They are not happy with having their own countries; they are compelled to enslave the entire planet to their proclivities.

FROM THE BOOK . . . AL ALDIEAYA . . .

It was clear, at least in Marten's mind, that these fanatics would never cease attacking Americans—home or abroad. Why otherwise reasonable people could not see that, as strictly an issue of power and religious zealotry, remains beyond him. They want us dead, and it will not end unless we allow them to destroy us or we are able to defeat them militarily no matter the haven, no matter the otherwise politically delineated state borders they hide within. It seemed the world was full of Neville Chamberlains, and very few had learned histories lesson!

FROM THE BOOK . . . COMIC RELIEF . . .

American comedian physician Hunter "Patch" Adams discovered that laughter helped the sick heal faster. Whether it be solely the chemical releases or temporarily distracting oneself from the illness or both was hardly relevant, it just was clear that laughter worked. A scientific study could never really fully quantify the theorem, but it is now widely accepted as true. It is not a case of Schrödinger Cat (the hypothetical cat that may be considered both alive and dead at the same time as a result of its fate being linked to a random subatomic event that may or may not occur). You cannot treat the same patient just with medicine and just with humor at the same time. You cannot clone a patient, at least not yet, to conduct such a true legitimate comparison on the same subject under both conditions.

The distance between a laugh and a good cry, is not a great expanse. Have you ever laughed so hard you began to cry? Conversely, tears can lead to giddiness. It can become present when acceptance is achieved, and we finally adapt. The merriment can only come if we realize how overly self-important, we allowed ourselves to be fooled into.

Humor, for Marten, became a double-edged sword. Indeed, he used it as a deflection at times he feels down. If we don't laugh, we'd be crying as the saying goes. Sometimes we just react; other times we choose how we respond to any given situation.

FROM THE BOOK . . . MISDIRECTION . . .

Truth be told it is not just the GIJIAS that spread such misgivings and strife amongst all peoples. Much information, of religious nature, has been lost over time and more hidden or censored by being withheld from the masses. Each faith, and what only makes sense to each religious conviction, is to pass on only the knowledge and wisdom that is desired to be bestowed upon its believers.

Humankind has only been able to grasp a certain degree of enlightenment, in regard to its own pretexts, let alone 'supposedly' conflicting creeds. The very nature of the separation of many denominations of the Christian faith demonstrates that fact. Some of the very foundations of the Christian faith beg question. It is demanded that 'faith' allow acceptance, and that all truth shall be imparted upon our ascension.

FROM THE BOOK . . . NAPERVILLE . . .

Theresa, while she thought she was fully mindful of the need to be a protector of her child, realized she was far more an ostrich on this topic than the mama bear she needed to be.

INTRODUCTION

*F*irst, I hope my writing style reflects my love of math classes over English classes (though I did take a few semesters of journalism and wrote for the school paper) when I was in school; despite my love of the written word, and more so my love to express my thoughts via my own written content; I hope it does not interfere with your reading enjoyment. However, this is me – this is how I write!

Who am I and from whence did I come? In my opinion, this is not an enormously relevant issue in whether you will enjoy this publication. Therefore, beyond just saying I'm old, well, of course, relative to you or not an open question. I was born in the early 1960s, and at least I sure feel old some days more than others. I am male, in case the name didn't give it away, and I was born and raised and happy to still be in Wyandotte, Michigan; well, actually I was born in a hospital the next city over, but anyway…

This is the part of the book where you might normally see an "about the author" diatribe. But like you are about to discover this is not your normal book, so there will not be an in-depth "my life and background" dive. I will also share, however, that I am a former information technology professional who has always written poems, short-stories—some copyrighted but never published—and even prior a novelette. This book is the culmination of the dream I had and a calling I felt to bring this work of combination fact and fiction to the world. I am very politically active in Michigan, including the newsletter editor and webmaster for a couple of my local political committees. If you really, really, really are interested in knowing all about my life, visit the Terror Strikes website: http://TerrorStrikes. info/about-the-author page.

The world is different today than when I grew up and had the typical interaction with the written and movie world, where the book was the book. That was it for your money. And the movie was the movie; it is no longer the case now. Every movie you buy on DVD or Blue ray comes with BONUS MATERIAL: behind the scenes, edited scenes, alternate scenes, or alternate endings. Therefore, I thought you deserve to see additional materials. Everything is online these days in some shape or related form, and, therefore, an additional materials part of your experience with this book is online where you can see a brief note about particular chapters or other reference materials. So, I'm offering this added online bonus offer FREE OF CHARGE.

I am telling you all this now, at the beginning of the book, before you get into the nitty gritty of the story rather than the end and will share those online links as an aside for while you are reading; if you want to go there is your option and then you can pick the book back up after your side-trip to the Internet. It is not necessary, however, for you to do so to enjoy the book (the story is sufficiently complete as-is in this version of the manuscript). This is just an option I offer in this not your normal average book experience. Otherwise, if you indeed choose to dive right in then afterward you can come back and revisit this intro to see which supplemental information might still interest you.

In the "Flashback" chapter, the notion of the "enemy of my enemy" concept is dealt with but not with direct reference to that phrase (such as when Russia was part of the Allies in WWII, and as happening at times with the "War on Terror" operations) – more at: https://tinyurl.com/EnemyOfMyEnemyNotion. Let me say upfront regarding this link – it is a brief, although admittedly odd, drive-by kind of article/blog based on a social media post making just a few statements to make the point. It is *not* indicative of most of my articles, which are far more detailed.

In the "Love Vs Fake Hate" chapter…

1. The article/blog referenced therein:
    https://tinyurl.com/ActualLoveVsFakeHateClaims

2. The other mass-slaughter of abortion is mentioned. Related:
    http://tinyurl.com/RoeVWadeExamined
    https://tinyurl.com/Gosnell2016
    https://tinyurl.com/BlackBabyGenocide
    Life matters! All Lives Matter!

3. Chapter references to modern "WOKEism" ("Political Correctness" on steroids). For more on aforementioned see:
    https://tinyurl.com/ActualLoveVsFakeHateClaims
    https://tinyurl.com/FakeWokeExposed

In the "9/11" chapter, the notion of the United States having a Judeo-Christian foundation is briefly mentioned but not expounded upon. There is not an immediate need for historical references this book is dealing with. A related piece you may wish to review, not going much into it, but instead is "Federalism" is online as "Federalists and Federalism (of today), nowhere near the same mold as our Founders (of yesteryear) that wrote the Federalist Papers (excerpts of my Sat. September 11, 2021 speech)" which is available online at: http://tinyurl.com/OriginalistFederalists. At this link are additional links to other (recorded) speeches where Kristina Karamo dives deeper into the religious foundations of the nation which, in my opinion, is very worthy of listening to. As well as I touch on in my recorded remarks beyond the written portions in the blog.

The "Comic Relief" chapter was potentially targeted for elimination and just some of its points relocated to other chapters. However, it did not land up being cut or trimmed, it appears in full in this final publication, including tribute to Jessica Star, Robin Williams, and others (RIP).

See also:

https://tinyurl.com/HelpPreventSuicide

https://tinyurl.com/WAAM-MOC-Suicide and https://tinyurl.com/WAAM-MOC-TeenSuicide (audio presentations)

Also, the serious end to the chapter, we are called to act, not just speak: http://tinyurl.com/2Chronicles714For2020 and (part 2) http://tinyurl.com/2Chronicles714For2022

"Laughlin" (originally titled "Sin City") is the complete chapter in this book. However, I just wanted to provide link to my article on Vegas written back in 2018: https://tinyurl.com/JLDVegasReview.

In the "YYZ" (which is the airport code for Toronto) chapter, I introduce the notion about twisting of language in today's "Political Correctness" / "Woke" (which I refer to as "Pathetical Corruptness") world. In order to justify policy positions, some try to redefine words or phrases, and sadly at times lie about the contents of whole books, including the Bible (aside from the denominational variations).

Related: https://tinyurl.com/LeftTwistsLanguage and latest being "Fair" addressed in: https://tinyurl.com/DefineFAIR.

There was to be a chapter titled "Sandwich," which I ultimately scrapped for space. It is, however, not going to be provided online for viewing as it only contained some brief asides; as you might garner from the title, the chapter wandered a bit too far afoul from the topic for any analogy or metaphor references to be of value to warrant inclusion but was to provide further character development that was ultimately moved elsewhere into the manuscript—and other rough notes for the chapter that then was never fully developed.

"Precursor" was another partially developed chapter, all of which was incorporated into other chapters. Certainly, then no need to share that other than this brief mention. "Precursor" chapter, we hardly knew thee, may you rest-in-peace. Yes, my humor is lame, and this foreshadows something you'll find in the book. LOL

"Terror Havens" was to be an additional chapter. The chapter was going to do a deep-dive into the various terror havens, nation-states sympathetic to terrorists tacitly or even some implicitly funding the camps or attack operations, various known and even suspected terror camps. Many are shocked to hear that we still have excursion troops in and out of Somalia, having thought we completely pulled out and were never to return after the *Blackhawk Down* incident. I decided on eliminating the long, drawn-out, potentially boring (for some) details, and leave it to the reader if they want to follow-up on searching out such information via a myriad of strictly nonfiction authors on the terrorism topic.

More (updates, added info/links) at:
http://TerrorStrikes.info/introduction

<u>Additional subject-matter related…</u>

Joseph M. Lenard on social media (most platforms): @JLenardDetroit.

Current platform for articles/blogs: http://tinyurl.com/JLDArticles.

The "War on Terror" like the Second World War has brought on some unlikely Allies at times: http://tinyurl.com/EnemyOfMyEnemyNotion.

Fascism in America (or, who are the modern Nazi's) is briefly mentioned (for detailed discussion) – see: https://tinyurl.com/todaysnazis.

Some seem to twist their faith, to fit their political agenda, rather than their faith shaping their politics as should be; or one's faith is clearly not so "primary" a concern in their life (detailed deep-dive on subject) – see: http://tinyurl.com/SomeTwistJesusWords.

The warping of language – For Greater Good and more: https://tinyurl.com/ForGreaterGood.

U. S. Constitution – 14th Amendment "…nor shall any State deprive any person of life…" Life matters! All Lives Matter!

This is NOT a book about death, but one about LIFE (and living) and of those (foreign and domestic) that would deprive others of that Life, Liberty, and Pursuit of Happiness.

Please help those in need (Pay It Forward) –
see: http://TerrorStrikes.info/charities.

Thank you,
Joseph M. Lenard

Updates (added info/links) to this Introduction will be added post-publication release at: http://TerrorStrikes.info/introduction.

FOREWORD
by Bruce Fleury

*J*oe Lenard's new book *Terror Strikes,* although a work of fiction, is especially timely and topical, particularly in view of America's inexplicable and precipitous withdrawal from Afghanistan in late 2021. In doing so, our nation disgraced itself when it abandoned the time-honored practice of "leaving no one behind," yes; but, more importantly, by doing so, the United States opened the door wide open to an increased terror threat by the Taliban, whose rapid takeover of a former ally sent Washington politicos' heads spinning, al Qaeda, whom we had previously crushed in the wake of the devastating September 11 terror attacks on New York City, Washington, DC and Stoystown, PA; ISIS, which we destroyed virtually overnight with ruthless efficiency, resolve, and force of arms; Islamic Jihad, Iran's Islamic Revolutionary Guard Corps and other groups sworn to destroy not only the U.S., Israel, and our allies in the Middle East, but Western civilization itself, and usher in a worldwide Islamic caliphate.

Joe's book examines the terror threat from a different angle, in that, as the author of this book, he looks at it from the perspective of Marten, the novel's protagonist who, himself, is writing a book of his own on this very subject. In addition, Joe provides his own commentary and insights at various points along the way, to ensure we never forget what happened at the hands of the monsters who, as George W. Bush reminded us in the wake of the 9/11 attacks, possess a hatred far in excess of their meager numbers. But Joe doesn't stop there; lest we forget the existential danger posed not only to this country, he also reminds us of other past terrorist actions in places like London, England, and Madrid, Spain, just to name a few.

Terror Strikes is the culmination of years-long effort Joe mounted that has finally come to fruition. And now, we all have the privilege of reading one man's (two men, actually, Joe and Marten) take on an international crisis that, if not addressed with more urgency, threatens to condemn our descendants to live in a 7th-Century nightmare from which there may very well be no awakening, if any.

We can't say we haven't been warned.

Bruce Fleury

BRUCE FLEURY IS–

Author of - *The Negro Project: Margaret Sanger's Diabolical, Duplicitous, Dangerous, Disastrous And Deadly Plan For Black America.*

Talk-show radio host – *the Abolitionists RoundTable (ART)* on *WAAM radio* Sat's 9 am: http://WAAMradio.com (*the Abolitionists RoundTable* Archives: http://tinyurl.com/ARTofMIArchives).

TERROR STRIKES

1

STORM

DO NOT KILL A SOUL WHICH ALLAH HAS MADE SACRED.

—Quran 6:151

*T*he sky burst open with the tremendous sound of a thunderbolt and the anticipation of the bright flash to follow. Marten's eyes darted, as they focused across the heavens, as he was eagerly looking forward to the beautiful, at least to him, calming sight; as he and his wife, Hope, had come to view these light shows in the night skies from their front porch. Usually, together, they watched for the streak of electrical charge that would light up the heavens. Not this instance, Marten stood alone, and the flash never came.

Marten has a fascination with thunderstorms in the otherwise tranquil sea of clouds, in any given evening's atmosphere where storms may dwell, but something was horribly wrong this night. This thunder was no ordinary thunder. This thunder echoed and billowed on, as he had never quite heard thunder do before.

1

Suddenly, it became obvious that this was indeed not thunder at all. The sound carried on seemingly forever, even though no discernable real time had passed by. Then, just as instantaneously as the clatter initiated it ceased, yet a secondary reverberation of seemingly indiscernible sound waves continued bellowing a loud static-filled sound, and, as he would soon discover, massive hurricane force winds would also soon be descending upon his slumber interrupted.

Marten's mind raced, firing electronic synapses rivaling the largest computer system, searching the caverns of the database of his memories to find a match of this seemingly new, but yet somehow familiar, intriguing sound. He lowered his gaze for a moment and then raised his brows slightly, and head tilted a fraction off level, as he came up blank within the recesses of his mind. Turning, once again, in the direction the thunder's flash should be appearing, he pursed his lips and squinted into the darkness, puzzled at what he was witnessing.

The rumbling eerily continued. The sky lit up with a flash of blinding light, but it was definitely not lightning. Instinctively, Marten raised his right hand to shield his eyes as he stumbled two small steps backward until he was against the vinyl siding of his still highly mortgaged ranch style Michigan home.

The morning breeze drastically changed direction. What started out, just a few short moments before, as a soft cool feeling upon his face, turned into a sort of suction - as if standing and having a humongous vacuum held in front of him. The low rumbles still resonated.

What was it? Where did it originate? How did it land up in his morning sky?

The questions quickly dissipated from his mind and were replaced with an overwhelming fear and dread. All expression erased from his face. With wide eyes he gazed upon the billowing clouds that quickly formed in front of him. At this point he wished it was only rain and lightning bolts filling his surroundings. Instead, he had thoughts of Alice in Wonderland falling down a rabbit hole and Dorothy saying, "we're not in Kansas anymore." He chuckled at the thoughts, but his situation clearly was no laughing matter.

"Dear Lord," he thought. "Please, take the wheel"—the new thoughts replacing his movie trivia lines.

Maybe the red glow that Marten thought he momentarily saw was the sun's rays refracting through the clouds, but more likely it was something far more sinister. This storm did not seem to be a natural, or nature-born, phenomena.

Suddenly, an unfamiliar, pungent scent of unknown origin began to fill his nostrils. Marten's knees became weak and began to buckle. He felt his whole body become lighter than air, yet his bone structure could not hold his body erect, he was flying, floating, yet falling, all at once. He became light-headed and his front porch seemed to spin around him, yet he remained in place. His body succumbed to the contradictions in gravitational effects; slowly he slouched down onto the hard, cold, dry boards of his front deck, succumbing to the ever-increasing heat. The waft of scents, rumbling thunder, and flashes of bright white light showered over him as he closed his eyes.

2

AWAKENING

IF YOU *WERE* PURE AND UPRIGHT,
SURELY NOW HE WOULD AWAKE FOR YOU,
AND PROSPER YOUR RIGHTFUL DWELLING.

—Job 8:6

*T*he nightmare remained the same. Marten's brow beaded with sweat. His head was throbbing, beating in time with the pulse of the blood coursing through his veins. A numbing sensation enveloped his brain and crept down the left side of his body. His heart beat unusually slow, unlike after awakening from most night terrors when his heart would race wildly, creating an impression that his heart would vibrate itself right out the encasement of his body.

Marten slumped onto his tingling left arm and hand, from the upright seated position his body was thrust into when the shooting pains raced through his nerve endings, causing the involuntary jolt to consciousness and into his current seated position, and out of the warm embrace of his wife. Hope woke quickly by her husband's quaking in their bed. She sat up and reached out for him, beckoning him to speak, pleading, praying for his pain to cease and "Come back to me, you can't leave me," she shouted.

He didn't hear her.

Hope desperately attempted to help Marten reconnect with reality, as this became an all-too-familiar event during their nights. That is, of course, on the nights that Marten could actually sleep. Nights like these were the worst. When Marten would require the use of a sleep aid, the chemical reaction provided an artificially deeper sleep, which was fertile ground for the trance-like state in which these dreams flourished. Hope feared that one night these night-terrors would cause her beloved to have a real heart-attack. She called out again while reaching for the alarm remote that called the emergency medical team link to save precious seconds if this were a real attack.

She stopped just short of pressing the glowing red button when she felt the cold, clammy right hand of her spouse of twenty-five years that now clasped her left hand that was on the bed. She turned her attention from the remote to her husband's hunched over body that appeared to be recovering but showed observable signs that his left side was still somewhat frozen in place and sending waves of pain pulsating throughout his neurological system.

"I'll be alright, dear," he assured Hope, but, unconvinced, she still clutched the emergency remote control within her right hand, with index finger poised to tap the alarm to signal a needed emergency medical team response. She pulled her left hand away and moved it to caress Marten's tingling left shoulder.

"Really, love," he tried to further reassure her as he raised his head taking in the cool tranquil color of their light blue bedroom and gazing even more skyward toward the cathedral ceiling mural of fluffy white clouds in the sky-blue background.

The bedroom décor was designed to provide a sanctuary in an otherwise chaotic world. These walls held back the reality, in which Marten had been able to shield the entire nation—even Hope—but no more! The dream invaded their nights and was uncontrollable after the public horror of September 11, 2001.

He turned his head back toward his beloved and met her penetrating gaze as his breathing began to normalize, and she eased her grip on the remote, letting it drop onto the king-sized bed. He leaned toward her now; she brought both her hands up and began to caress his face. Words were not necessary; Marten knew how concerned his wife was regarding these dreams that further aggravated his, tenuous at best, ability to get a reasonably sound night sleep.

They nestled together now in the bed, backs to the headboard, drawing closer and embracing. They kissed, lightly. Hope broached the silence. "It would help if you talked to me about it," she said.

Marten didn't provide a verbal response but communicated with an all too familiar glance that indicated his displeasure about his wife's unwelcome commentary.

Knowing full well he wouldn't want to discuss it, Hope pressed the issue. "You know you need to address this with me sooner or later," she insisted. "I will not let this drop."

"Damn it, dear," Marten huffed.

"You know, I cannot believe you," Hope insisted. Confident that Marten's full attention was restored now, she replaced the remote to its location on the headboard but never diverting her gaze from him.

"I have never seen any evidence from any sources to suggest that any terrorist has come close to having use of an atomic or nuclear enhanced explosive. I cannot make it any clearer than that," he volunteered though his displeasure grew in intensity, and bordered on outright anger now as he fidgeted more upright and shed the bedding with his left hand. He continued, "nor is anyone even coming close to being able to use an atomic or nuclear enhanced explosive outside full state-run nuclear powers," leaving out the instability of Iran and potentially Pakistan that could aid terrorist's development of such weapons, or outright just sell them to unstable forces that ignore the mutually assured destruction (M.A.D.) deterrence concept that has kept the planet free from nuclear war. Marten continued his protestations. "I cannot make it any clearer than that," he said, hoping it would end the interaction.

But, no, he sensed Hope was going to make another comment thus ruining his chances for getting back to sleep. Still, he was not going to let this turn into another lengthy discussion. "End of story," he interjected. "I don't need you constantly adding additional and undue pressures on me, and you know that."

She withdrew but a look of concern still filled her face. Hope had convinced herself that Marten had received such insight and was just attempting to shield her from the frightening reality such capabilities in the wrong hands would bring suddenly upon peoples unwittingly going about their days.

Marten was aware of the delicate balance between reporting the news and providing the truth, but without the sensationalist claims of tabloid papers. He worked for a respected Detroit newspaper, after all, and they were responsible for presenting the truth and avoiding panic and paranoia that sadly some media outlets specialized in.

Marten, and the rest of the editors were exercising some self-restraint, but Hope had implied that the nation's newspapers were purposefully misleading the country. As if there were not some real government conspiracies, necessary secrets they argue, to keep the public in the dark as to the actual degree of terrorist threats in the United States, which the massively increased and empowered homeland security agencies have, some would argue, unwarranted and outside the constraints of the US Constitution, to try to intercede overseas to prevent. The very notion was just so absurd to anyone within the news industry. They didn't believe it could really happen with all the current heightened alerts sending the alphabet agencies like the CIA and FBI, into a flurry of preemptive actions rather than their normal defensive postures, but the masses accepted that one day the terrorists would have their hands on such powerful advanced weapons. For now, a collective delusion must hold: it cannot, it will not, happen.

No professional, at least one that respects American lives, news agency was going to induce a panic over activities that did not currently exist, at least not with one hundred percent evidence. The news that was available to report on was sensational enough, there was no need to manufacture any.

Marten climbed out of bed, his mind now churning over and over the insanity, as he viewed it, of his wife's controversy. He was certainly not going to be able to get back to sleep very fast, if at all for the remainder of the night, now. He rubbed his eyes, trying to clear the remaining cobwebs from the sleeping aid which was specifically designed to provide a time released dose to assist a complete night's sleep, but this interruption was countermanding its full abilities to complete its purpose.

"I can't believe you did this to me again," he said as he walked from the room.

Hope, of all people, Marten believed, should accept his assurances. He didn't expect all the wild conspiracy theorists that purport to every newspaper in America had succumbed to censorship at the hands of the United States government rather than earnest restraint to reporting solely factually double sourced information to understand that reality, but his wife!? He fully expected her to agree to his guarantee.

Marten had always freely offered his 'opinions and beliefs' as to what truly lay behind the basic hard and cold facts as reported in his employer's publication. From the complex to the mundane, Marten always freely discussed the news of the day with his wife. He discussed all kinds of topics, whether the guilt or innocence of those arrested locally, the underlying truth of political corruption cases, or the spin supporters and foes alike would use to cloud the situations. Issues of war or peace. Even the basic entertainment value of the chances of the Lions to aspire above their traditional seasons, year in and year out, of mediocrity.

Self-restraint in the name of public safety was not censorship. All the managing staff fully believed that. Not instilling a panic in the masses was not concealing facts for the benefit of the government. Allowing the US to maintain secrecy in the name of the national security interest as opposed to reporting every detail of US policy and actions to the enemy was being responsible. The First Amendment to the Constitution was not under attack, nor at risk; at least there was no real threat from government sources, only those wanting to bolster their agendas. As time would pass, some news agencies would cave to certain political pressures to protect presidents and provide political cover over non-related national security policy issues.

Since 9/11 President Bush and others that followed were going to need a certain level of secrecy and like it or not some would need to delegate to Homeland Security certain tasks for 'plausible deniability' when engaging in press conferences.

There was censoring of news, then there was shaping of it, as some of the very same people used such a narrowly focused definition of weapons of mass destruction when it came to Iraq and its capabilities that even the *New York Times* later reported massive stashes of chemical weapons were found without any sense of irony. Later, after engaging in "lies by ommission" and later pivoted when they outlined on their pages in an easy-to-follow graphic that seemed to now bolster the position for the Iraq invasion, they wanted a broad definition of the term to fit their agenda others used to oppose. These people reported that specific stores of yellow cake were not found even though everyone knew that Saddam had moved some stores of weapons to Syria. Even after the beginning of Civil War in Syria where some US troops were engaged, and still engaged in as a protective quick-reaction force in southern Syria in part to try and ensure the rebels or Assad's forces don't spill over into Israel, dragging them into the conflict.

This topic of weapons and whether they are viable provides an endless frustration to any agency trying to provide news and information within a consistent framework.

Fear mongering, on the one hand, and eristic claims of sensationalism, on the other, were levied when they reported that nerve gas artillery shells were uncovered in the Iraqi desert after the toppling of Saddam Hussein. Sure, it was and still is a debatable sore point as to how much was left over from the Iran and Iraq War—and sure, these warheads could have been lost following the conflict—versus how much was purposefully buried and known to the command structure for potential use later. Although it's debatable, it didn't matter. Too many people were more than happy to lay claims that it was nothing more than apologia squib for the invasion hawks.

The converse would be alleged when any rumors would surface for political posturing to attack a person or party position for the failure to provide report about how little merit the charges may hold. The problem, of course, is that legitimate newspapers are not in business to dispel rumor but to report genuine and justifiable factual stories.

Marten wandered down the hall, through the living-room, and into the kitchen while his mind was relitigating old whether or not to report situations. Just what he planned on doing once he reached his destination he wasn't quite sure. He was more or less on autopilot. His mind was too consumed by thoughts of the dilemma over reports of terrorists, their plots, and the government's activities aimed at capturing these fanatics before they had a chance to strike and kill innocent civilians again—not to mention trying to deter or intervene in the early stages of the formation of any new clusters of would-be attackers, like when al Qaeda waned, and ISIL/ISIS rose.

The pressures of the standard day-to-day reporting of the news to the general public had always been burdensome. The terrorist threat since 9/11, however, had ushered in a heightened dimension. There would always be critics. People would always criticize almost any story, looking for slants and biases or questioning the very facts being reported. It was amazing how people could read the same story and come away with a notion of a 'right-wing' conservative or 'left wing' liberal inference; despite the care taken to maintain neutral ground in those days following 9/11, then into the Iraq War, and beyond with Presidential successions as inevitable with term-limits existing on our Presidents, but many of the same lunatics, to Marten's mind, left to stay forever in Congress.

No matter how carefully sensitive facts were being handled, the paper would receive an onslaught of calls and letters generated claiming the newspaper is either withholding information or providing too much information so as to either shield or promote the terrorist's point of view. In the balance lay the prosecution of those responsible, the protection of the innocent, and the very lives of those who these would be terrorists would terminate without prejudice.

Marten found himself peering into the refrigerator. He had apparently meandered the last steps and opened the door without conscious thought. Their cat had now decided to join him and affectionately began rubbing on his leg. Marten then glanced down in the direction of Speedy.

"Good idea," he conceded. "Milk it is!"

While it wasn't their habit, Marten decided to give Speedy a saucer of milk since his purring spurred Marten to warm up some in order to assist his return to sleep, he thought Speedy deserved a minor award of sharing some of the 2% reduced fat beverage. Marten took hold of the carton and motioned Speedy away from the refrigerator door, so he could close it. Speedy meowed enthusiastically in the hopes that he would indeed be receiving some white liquid.

Marten pulled a small pan from the nearby cupboard, as well as a cup for himself and a saucer for Speedy. After starting some milk to warming on the stove, he poured a small amount onto the saucer and presented it to the eagerly awaiting cat, who graciously accepted the offer with meows, purrs, and additional rubs up and down Marten's shins.

"Stop nudging me, silly," Marten demanded. "You're gonna make me spill your milk." Speedy, Marten was certain, didn't understand nor care, but they had always treated their pets as fur babies and one of the family—and respectful conversation remained a part of their relationship.

Marten took a brief moment to sidetrack his mind from his current thought process to fondly recall the day he, Hope, and his three girls (Brandy, Paula, and Tamara) went over to the Detroit Animal Shelter to rescue Speedy. They didn't know what his name was before making their way into the shelter and being one of so many animals in need of a rescue. But he is most assuredly "Speedy" now and living large in their home. He gets plenty of love from the kids, plenty of window space to stare out at the passing neighbors and seems to have been very people friendly from the start. Hopefully he wasn't traumatized too long out on the streets before he was picked up and made available for a new loving family to adopt him.

Marten turned off the burner and transferred the lukewarm milk from the pan and into the cup. He took a brief sip while placing the pan into the kitchen sink. He noticed Speedy had made quick order of his morning treat and scooped up the saucer to add alongside the pan. He rinsed the saucer, placed it in the sink, added some water into the pan, and turned to move to the kitchen table to have a seat.

Fortunately, Marten had already scheduled today as a personal day in order to try and get some additional rest, so he would be able to return to bed and to sleep in for some of the morning hours he would otherwise be spending at the office. As part of his personal day, he contemplated spending some time in the den to work on his own project, attempting to write his first book.

As he sipped his temperate drink, he briefly patted Speedy on the head, who was no doubt hoping for a second offering. While Speedy's purring underneath his loving strokes provided some additional sense of calm, his mind returned to thoughts of his nightmare, and the impetus for his book project. Writing about the root of his concerns—terrorist attacks of the past, present, and potential future—as part of the process, he hoped would ease his mind and maybe relieve his nightmares.

Marten realized the indefectible truth that the war against terrorism was the ultimate existential fight of good versus evil. It is the undeniable struggle of those who desire all mankind to live in peace and prosperity against those whose hate is based on jealousy, blind bigotry, unrestrained power, and unjustified and irrational religious notions.

Marten thought about how these GIJIA (Global Islamic Jihad Interim Army) or GIJIAS (Global Islamic Jihad Interim Army Soldiers) members, believers, and supporters, misguided by personal scars that foment hatred, desire for power, and vengeance, are driven to kill.

Misconceived and distorted notions of non-Islamic peoples provide a fertile ground to weave the deceptive seeds of hate. This perverse conjecture of lumping entire classes of people into one prejudiced assembly, of course, is not limited to today's terrorist hate mongers, but it has never before been such a prevalent and destructive force.

Marten knew that GIJIA consist of the most extreme Islamic/ Muslim radicals, fundamentalists, and, as some would even point out correctly, fascists. It is quite clear that these individuals, and those that support them, believe that they are the only ones qualified to determine what is moral and good and that they must impose those beliefs on the world. They are not happy with having their own countries, they are compelled to enslave the entire planet to their proclivities.

An issue of education and perspective exists. Somehow people have come to equate fascism with Nazi-ism. While synonymous in respect to 1930s Germany, it is not mutually exclusive across the board. While all Nazi's, members of the National Socialist Deutschland Arbeiter Party (NSDAP) during the Second World War, were fascists in nature, not all fascists are Nazi's. Many modern fascists agree to the precepts of use of control through regulations of businesses for benefit of the state and the ruling elites, without a direct takeover of ownership attributed to communism. How there really are not significantly demonstrable differences, Marten wondered how people could not grasp.

He thought about how fascism rose during the 1930s in Italy and in Spain also. Fascism is sweeping through the Middle East today, with Iran being the most prevalent and dangerous. The same scenario of appeasement leading to an emboldened and belligerent leadership is dangerously on the same path of a seemingly inevitable conflict.

The question for many is whether the world will have the courage to stand up to the global threat posed by these fascist nations before an entire global conflict breaks out or not.

With those notions of business regulation, along with roving bands of Hitlerian like Brownshirts or Mussolini's Blackshirts, rioting, looting, and burning down communities seemingly only in people of color neighborhoods, is the whole issue of fascism in our own homeland. The argument for some forms of fascism (as evidenced with the even further Wuhan-virus dictates) has crept into the United States. But that was and is a topic for a whole other book.

Marten reflected on the fact that some Americans had become so spoiled, they came to loathe their own nation that afforded them all they have. With such a meager sense of proportion and perspective, they are weak and easily manipulated by those who can take advantage of them to hate their own nation. They blame everyone else for their first-world problems, much like an entire nation was brainwashed into blaming Jews for their problems after which they were isolated and then outright murdered. Much ill can be done as long as there is personal gain, power, money, or even just a sense of belonging to something bigger.

Oh sure, everyone says "it cannot happen here," but even America went so far as to put Japanese Americans into camps during the Second World War. Whether or not it is indeed going to happen here is put on the back burner as it is most certainly escalating to such extremes in some locales abroad. To struggle against it will require military might and yet the most basic and gentle characteristics of human kindness. Most Christians, Jews, and mainstream Muslims alike wish to teach joy and peace and not degradation and oppression; unfortunately, there are evil individuals that exist within every categorization of peoples. That the complete abject hatred and disdain of any class, or group, of people is an unholy notion in any religion.

The question of 'fairness' being 'politically correct' throughout America has clouded norms once deemed as simple commonsense approaches to securing the nation and other national policies creep. For example, Marten thought about the fascist socialist version of nationalizing health care is another form of power and control in American Left movements, as they were NSDAP (Nazi) platform items, albeit under new more flowery terms and language to hide the direct comparisons that would easily otherwise be made under even a casual examination. When a party has twenty-eight planks of the Nazi platform within theirs, and they refuse to even broach the subject, can it, could it, would it, potentially go even further? Will intolerance reach the degree to which led to a Holocaust? No one wishes the nation to return to the degree of intolerance that led to the incarceration, without due process, of Japanese Americans during the Second World War. The United States concentration camps, while not the same degree of enslavement and genocide as the European camps, were evil in their own right.

In a country that has a constitution to protect free speech, Marten was concerned at the degree of intolerance toward the intolerant; within reason he was witnessing. The Bill of Rights was designed to protect minority opinion, and even opinions and speech that some, perhaps even at times the many, do not appreciate. Though there is a large degree of difference in speech that one may 'hate' and actual "hate speech," which courts had ruled time and again as being protected under the Constitution.

You may have heard that crying "Fire!" in a crowded theater is *not* a matter of opinion, or free speech, but when said fire is absent the "cry" made in "fraud" then becomes a matter of fraud and related laws and nothing to do with free speech and opinion. This is correct. Unless one can prove otherwise that there was no real expectation that a fire existed and the "cry" was not inadvertent and was ill-intent, beyond a reasonable doubt proven in court, the person is innocent.

Also, the world has become confused between the differences in hate speech, a touchy issue and is protected under the First Amendment, and speech that people just claim to hate. These people should be shunned perhaps, but unless their speech goes into conspiring to do harm, they must be allowed to exercise their freedoms of speech and association. It is lawful until it becomes a matter of the infringement of others' rights! If someone becomes violent or otherwise breaches the rights of those they disapprove, then the law can and must intercede.

To place under scrutiny and surveillance members of the Italian, German, and Japanese communities in this country was just plain prudent as we were at war with those nations. It is likewise a commonsense approach to provide additional scrutiny and attention to those who look Arabic, but not wholesale roundup and incarceration. While terrorist attacks continue to be perpetrated by those who fit that profile, it is only common sense to pay more attention to those within that group. To do so is not a violation of equal protections under the law, not if valid profiling of other characteristics for other crimes are also scrutinized under the law. There is a legal difference between "profiling" and unjust broad-brush stereotyping of an entire class of peoples.

While most white-collar crime is committed by middle-aged Caucasians, so profiling old white people makes sense when monitoring for those types of criminal activities. If all of a sudden, terrorist attacks were being committed by blonde-haired, blue-eyed persons, then it would only be correct to provide *equal* scrutiny to those who would also now fit that *profile*. These profiles only become prejudiced and discriminatory when the profiles themselves are without basis and merit, hateful broad-brush stereotyping.

The continued harassment of individuals not acting suspicious and not within the 'profile' of the crimes we are trying to prevent is an absurd notion. To allow oneself to be put under the additional scrutiny, if one fits the profile, needs to be viewed as a positive step of a proud and patriotic American. To be willing to care enough about our society and fellow citizens to undergo the added analysis will allow us to remain a free society, not endanger it.

What most people miss, Marten's figured, is that if security did start profiling specific looking people, the terrorists would then just recruit new terrorists that do not fit the profile as though it were that simple. That act alone, having to recruit members not fitting the profile of their usual recruiting base opens the terrorist organizations up for detection, if not outright infiltration, by investigatory agencies. Forcing the terrorists out into the open is exactly what will provide the greatest opportunity to stop major terrorist plots. Also, the complication of diversifying their jihadists forces is not high on their list of things to do as they are fundamentalists, and they lose part of their narrative (narrowly defined "us against the world") if they lose, in part, their fundamental make up and perhaps dilute their distrust and hatred of Western culture.

Marten had only recently come to these conclusions.

3

AL ALDIEAYA

WHOSOEVER KILLS A HUMAN BEING WITHOUT
[ANY REASON LIKE] MANSLAUGHTER,
OR CORRUPTION ON EARTH,
IT IS AS THOUGH HE HAD KILLED ALL MANKIND.

—Quran 5:32

*M*arten's phone rattled across the desk at his bedside. Reaching over in the dark, he picked it up and cradled it and its dim light penetrated the dark with a faint glow. A text message relayed in from the nearby phone network tower.

Invisible pulses of energy carrying encoded digital zeros and ones to make up the matter stream identifying the information packet to ensure that the one, and only the one (unless the NSA was illegally intercepting), phone that was the intended destination of the message would decode it. The phone, upon confirmation that it is the intended recipient, then places the memorandum into the phone's inbox.

Marten's interest was heightened, and he wiped his hands across his eyes in order to better focus his sight and bring himself to a greater consciousness. Two words appeared: Go Go's. He need not review the identifying source; this could only be from one person—Nicolas. It was a meaningless message to anyone who would read it outside of the two of them, as it referred to the pop group the Go Go's song titled "Vacation!" Inside code for time for getaway, a meet-up of some sort; best to stay away from traditional electronic communications methods.

Nic, Nicolas Anderson, and Marten went way back. They had developed, slowly, over time, a mutual respect built over years of honored promises of secrecy and give and take in the name of public greater good.

The FBI agent would never condone such a close relationship between a senior agent and a conveyer of information via the liberal press medium of the Detroit area newspaper for which Marten was employed early on during his years assigned to Detroit. In time, the uneasy give and take between the right of public to be informed of the truth, by means of the Detroit press, and the bureau's need to maintain evidence of ongoing investigations, indeed eased in his mind, and he saw the benefits of helping ensure information was correct over speculative.

Nic, eventually, welcomed the opportunity to have access to the press to ensure truth prevailed. More so the prospect of having the close nit relationship allowed him to influence certain aspects of a story release, or suppression in the name of security. He had finally come to learn that there were responsible members of the press, versus some that never learned the adage "Loose Lips Sink Ships" from the

Second World War, and that they would be willing to cooperate if it served the public interest. All bets were off, of course, if it was obvious other area papers were covering, or more importantly going to "break," a story and competitive interests came into play. There would be no sense in holding back information for a potentially less sensitive time of release, if it were just going to be provided by the other papers in town.

Everything had changed on 9/11, though the country was operating on an unopposed group assumption that the nation would not be altered. The media viewed its role differently. There was no government conspiracy to control or censor the news. The media outlets adopted, at least at first after 9/11, their own sets of control and restraint, not conspiratorially but due to a like-minded self-awareness, at the same time and across most of the print and television media and an empathetic public very understanding of the need.

The economy after 9/11 was greatly affected, certainly normal stimulus effected the changes, but the World Trade Center attacks of September 11, 2001, had added an exponential component to the slow in economic growth the United States was laboring under, and there was no assurance it would end quickly as the uncertainty following the 9/11 attacks would linger for some time. It had become a hidden, unspoken element underneath all the other factors.

Adding to the uncertainty, distrust, fear, new conspiracy theorists labeled 'Truthers' strains took hold. Folks who insisted that not only did the US government know, but actually, conspired with the Jews to do it to ourselves, adding a variant of anti-Semitism. It is, of course, one thing to suggest that the United States government may have received some information that could have prevented an attack, a deadly tragedy, and for whatever reasons could not "connect the dots," thereby failing to take action to intercede. It is another to claim actual, conspiratorial, calculation that allowed an event to occur. Then a whole other thing to succumb to the notion that the federal government itself would take an active role in the undertaking of a terrorist action against its identifiable citizens on its own soil.

Those who did not have the benefit of a close relationship with a government official, an insider of some sort, found agencies and their employees reaching out to open previously adversarial closed lines of communication, at least for some time before the deep-rooted suspicions of the agencies would again resurface, opened and eased for a time. Stakes had not been as high since the attack on Pearl Harbor, which was eerily analogous in the minds of many.

Not only were there the issues of national security, but also the economy. Peoples' livelihoods were at stake. A potential recession, if not full-on depression, could result if measures were not taken to "promote the general welfare" as outlined in our founding documents. Certainly, normal stimuli effected the changes, reducing regulations to allow the free flow of commerce and the like, but the WTC attacks of September 11, 2001, added an exponential negative component to other slowing factors creeping in before it that the United States was grappling under. It had become a not-so-hidden, though often attempted to be unspoken to not overly concern and panic people beyond the fear purveying "the new normal" everyone was trying to find, element underneath all the other factors. A more in-depth analysis of the causes and effects of everything distressing the country was now in order, needed, mostly welcomed.

The New York papers were seemingly more interested, in a Neville Chamberlainesque way, in appeasing our enemies. As the joke around the Detroit offices went, they were "the official paper of al Qaeda" for their often-muted reporting, seemingly afraid they might offend those that attacked us. The left-wing narrative that everything is America's fault, that we somehow were responsible, and it was inevitable that they would strike-back at the colonial invaders, is a false narrative. Certainly, there were always outlets that took a bias of the state to which they belonged. During the 1930s the Nazi's made sure that loyalists to them first and the nation itself second took place. People would, of course, always think of *Pravda* as more apparatchik than reporting honestly, especially during the Soviet years in Russia and clear Putin and Russian Communist Party propaganda now during their invasion, now second excursions (as prior just into Crimea), into Ukraine.

One of conservative radio-show host and author Mark Levin's best sellers was *Unfreedom of the Press* about the, in many peoples' minds, lurch toward those Pravda days by many papers here in the West—more Marxist propaganda purveyors than press the founders of America would ever envision could become.

The founders placed freedom of the press as the first of the Amendments, as several of the founders engaged in press activities themselves. They believed that a free press guarantee was essential to holding a government, any government, accountable. Sure, even the founders' early releases had a bias, a bias toward individual freedoms, personal responsibility, self-governance, and the like—the bedrock principles of the nation they hoped they could, and did, bring about. They rallied against tyranny of an oppressive regime; they could have never imaged a day when American papers would become advocates against the foundations of the nation itself and more so advocates for tearing down our own system rather than opposing those who would induce a tyranny, over promoting the American Dream and freedom everywhere.

None, however, was indicative of the sense of complete and abject bias and propaganda for a tyrannical and destructive cause than al Aldieaya. Al Aldieaya, with sympathetic nation-state governments to the cause of the GIJIAS, was founded and funded, to the thoughts of most in the West, to spread the GIJIAS message via favorable spin or outright falsification of facts: a direct tool of the potential caliphate coming.

Just as the American Left looked to rewrite much of America's history, craft it, spin it, emphasize negative aspects, in order to shape minds and make them more open toward moving more toward socialism, so too al Aldieaya was meant to, in part, muddy historical truths by presenting only a partially focused viewpoint and only presenting that which bolstered such GIJIA positions.

So many had forgotten that the West warred with Islamic fundamentalism before—the history of what became the Crusades and all the modern distortions, which were a response to Islamic aggressions, to protect Christians, to reclaim lands lost. Even more-so, it was a mystery how Americans could forget even when the Marine hymn touts: "from the Halls of Montezuma to the Shores of Tripoli." How is it that Americans do not know the reasons Tripoli is mentioned? That Islamic Pirates would seize ships from Western nations, steal its cargo, enslave its crews. Fighting on the shores of Tripoli was the necessary response by President Jefferson.

It was, before 9/11, unfathomable that media outlets in the United States might go so far as to appease the old enemy resurgence. It seemed to Marten's co-workers that the NYC outlets, several of them, and their ilk across the country, were interested in trumpery that advanced an agenda as opposed to truth heretofore unseen. Blustery and bombastic reports of misprision, rather than the *ne plus ultra* of print media they would have people believe they are. A collection of distorted facts that thinly guise their own desires and objectives, sometimes clearly in league with our enemies' anti-capitalism, willingness to curtail freedoms, in common with the desire of those attacking us to bring US Citizens to heal and make them more pliable, controllable, brainwashed and placated to accepting others directing every aspect of their daily lives.

How could it be since 9/11 that those wanting to destroy us and force-convert our lives and our system of governing would not now awaken to that some in our own nation were looking to do the same. As for now, though, it was the external enemy as the greatest threat and distraction from intrusions and the ever-growing numbers of domestic enemies.

It was clear, at least in Marten's mind, that these fanatics would never cease attacking Americans—home or abroad. Why otherwise reasonable people could not see that, as strictly an issue of power and religious zealotry, remains beyond him. They want us dead, and it will not end unless we allow them to destroy us or we are able to defeat them militarily no matter the haven, no matter the otherwise politically delineated state borders they hide within. It seemed the world was full of Neville Chamberlains, and very few had learned histories lesson!

The tape released on September 2, 2006, by al Zawahiri with Californian Adam Gadahn, one of the few American converts and Jihadists useful idiot, also known at the time as "Azzam the American" and jokingly referred to as "Shazam the Ameri-Ham" by Marten's colleagues, demanded that Christians convert to Islam. Not, of course, to the Islam that Muslims in America recognized and adhered to, but the harsh and rigid version of Islamism as a governmental system not just a religious model. Though, everyone knew that there were likely other al Qaeda sympathizers and Mosques that were fronts to Islamic indoctrination, recruitment, and potential terrorist centers for contact and conspiring.

The American Islamist, however, was so brainwashed and consumed by hatred, he likely believed and justified the propaganda of "We will not let them be" — "Yes, it is okay to attack ordinary people" generally goes against the Geneva accords—and "it is the fault of those [UK / USA] countries that they needed to attack us rather than just live their own lives to their own accords" false narrative rather than obsess over how others may be living their lives.

Marten and friends didn't want to offend the millions of peaceful and tolerant Arabs and Muslims – as, of course, not all Arabs are Muslim nor all Muslims Arab. The militants, however, were fair game at belittlement. In fact, these pathetic excuses for human beings needed to be demeaned as well as their militaristic, actual colonial intentions. As they would add, they "wouldn't want to insult their intelligence, if they had any intelligence to insult" that is. If it were not for the death and destruction that these fanatics wrought, they would be a laughing matter. How anyone could be taking their mindless, unwarranted, hatred and perversion of some aspects, versus the whole, of the Islamic holy and other writs seriously was just a mad proposition.

The years of Usama bin Laden's constant claims that the Jihad was concerning the United States "occupation" of Saudi Arabia, welcomed and appreciated by the Crown, was a clear smoke screen. How did anyone believe this? Marten mused. After all, the Terrorists on 9/11 thought nothing of killing fellow innocent Muslims that also were at the WTC that day.

When the United States called bin Laden's bluff by announcing withdrawal from Saudi soil for planned redeployment to such Arab states as Qatar, the UAE, Kuwait—the smaller nations that would be unable to defend themselves against their larger neighbors that may aggress—and as demonstrated when Saddam had previously invaded Kuwait and the first Gulf War resulting, bin Laden and al Qaeda changed their excuses for their hatred. This demonstrated that any attempts to placate or appease them would just exacerbate them, and that Usama followers would remain open to any of his ad hominem ramblings. Any attempts to appease would just result in more demands for concessions. Again, people fail to grasp the very basic concept of "you give evil an inch, it will reach for the next mile."

Again, Marten thought to himself, they want us dead, and it will not end unless we allow them to destroy us or we are able to completely eradicate them from the planet at worst, but hopefully at least pin them into an area or areas that they can easily be watched and kept from striking others. Otherwise, they would never stop.

Pacifism, in Marten's mind, if this is indeed the throws of an eventual full-on new world war, might only bring a longer and more drawn-out potential conflict—either between political ideologies or religious mistrust and hatreds. The question for him, in terms of Nostradamus, the sixteenth century prophet known to many as "*the man who saw time*," is will 'the head of the serpent that would cause such devastation and destruction as the world had never seen before' be dealt with to prevent such destruction. When you know your enemy is about to strike, preemptive action can be a form of self-defense.

The alternative is for people to stick their heads in the sand like an ostrich, or appeasement, in Chamberlain methodology, and just let the seeds of Armageddon grow. The choices we make today will have consequences on our tomorrows. Will we, potentially once more, ignore the lessons of history and allow ourselves to repeat, what hindsight has shown to be, our mistakes?

The GIJIAS psychology is one only about inflicting terror. They intend to make mayhem and act irrationally, while in the name of our desire to live in peace used against us and grant concessions to appease a would-be aggressor in hopes they will then learn to go-along with them to get-along narrative.

Marten hoped that his manuscript, a book on terrorism to be titled *Terrorist Tracks*, his accumulated knowledge, would bring to a public forgotten knowledge about 9/11, truth that might reawaken and open an honest debate. It would be his first book, and therefore is a big "bite" to chew, that he felt compelled to write.

Terrorist Tracks, a play on both tracking terrorists and terrorism over the years as well as the fact that, at least abroad, one of the favorite targets of jihadists is passenger trains— 'track' vehicles. If he could rouse one individual to the potential danger that they may not have considered, who then may stir another, to get people alert and paying attention that some things are more important than self and that wishful thinking or disregarding peril will not make it disappear. Like an ostrich that may literally bury its head in the sand, the dangers around it remain and can and likely will harm it.

Even if the United States changed its Constitution and declared the nation an Islamic republic, Americans would still be hated—in the minds of this enemy a perpetual envy and covetousness of America's freedom and wealth, haves versus have-not dynamics, the same thinking and sentiment of American liberals. They want what we have. They will think nothing of stealing it one way or another.

Many people, and Islamists, fit into this pattern perfectly, will do anything to suit their agenda, and when facts are not on their side, they ignore the facts or try to twist them to fit their narrative, to fit within their preconceived notion, per contra to reviewing all the facts and reaching one's open determination of any issue based upon truths. You hear it, the Left's constant twisting of language. When facts do not fit their narrative, they spin a version they call "their truth!" All blatant jealousy and hatred for those living the so-called American Dream. Hatred for the American way of life, liberty, and freedoms to pursue one's own happiness, and less to do with religion—despite religion being used as a divisive tool to incite, promote, and foster more hatred and separation as means to their power and ability to control others. To force an equity of outcome, versus an equality of opportunity.

Usama bin Laden seemed to see himself as a new Muhammad—or worse, as more powerful and of greater all-consuming importance as imbued by God, above that of the original Muslim prophet. The new prophet, that much seemed certain, was an ultimate soi-disant leader, the peremptory false prophet with a political manifesto, rather than holy writ, of destruction.

The rodomont bin Laden's ego seemed to know no boundary. His cave dwelling, and later his hideout in Pakistan that ultimately saw his doom at the hands of US Special Forces, lotusland provided a ploy to further his crony requirements, and to attempt to deny his heritage. Deny his birthright of privilege and wealth, that so many forget his roots of Saudi royalty, resource abundance, and license. While residing in caves with greater appointments than the poorest of the poor, he sought to dupe those into his movement.

4

TULSA

*H*ope and the kids knew that while Marten was in the study not to bother him. They had learned over time that interrupting him would only prolong the duration of his stay behind the closed door. By letting Marten keep his focus, he would be able to be available sooner than if his work was fractured and episodic. Marten required a large degree of concentration to ensure he retained his focus to complete any duties required for whatever tasks remained.

Marten would sometimes be required to expand or contract reports just before deadlines, perform last-minute fact verification, formulate strategies on whether to hold or proceed with a story, quickly input a last-minute scoop so as to not pass on the opportunity of an exclusive. The sacrifice was the necessary trade-off for the increased added value of allowing Hope to remain home and be full-time parent for the children and still be able to maintain their lifestyle. For the sake of the children, it was a commitment they willingly accepted. But today, the time was to be spent on working on his book.

Marten and Hope had also discussed at length the added value, as well as the additional strain that writing a book would require of the family. Hope, again, agreed to the shorter-term aggravation and frustration of the added workload on Marten and the demands of time that would further keep him away from quality time with her and the family for their longer term benefit.

They decided that Marten would take on the task of writing his manuscript before the window of opportunity may pass. Within a few years, they would scale back their lives regardless of whether their financial goals were met, and they would make any necessary adjustments over the next few years to attain that goal and to improve the quality and time together.

Hope also knew that this was part therapy for her beloved. That releasing his pent-up apprehensions into a written release may relieve his mind of some of his tensions, knowing the things tormenting him many nights may help others while helping himself to compartmentalize, organize, work through his trepidations over the amount of time that had passed without a major, massive, one-up from the previous terrorist strike and his never-ending dread that the next big one must just be around the corner.

No matter how many terrorist leaders the Western world tracked down and eliminated as a threat—via the more expeditious and cleaner, in so far as not risking American lives with boots on the ground like the Usama raid, drone strikes—only one thing was assured. There would be another eager, hate-filled, opportunist ready, willing, and able to fill their shoes and continue the Usama legacy and potentially kill Americans abroad and threaten, nay promise, that they would again hit us in North America. Whether it took a decade or two, or three, until they could hit us hard with another large-scale assault, they would engage in a death-by-a-hundred-cuts approach to ensure their strategy stayed moving forward, and while we ourselves vowed to never forget, they too swore they would never let us forget their lust for spilling Western culture's blood.

While Western culture tries to teach our children to be accepting, tolerant, and loving, even to our enemies, in the Judeo-Christian ethic tradition, they indoctrinate theirs with endless propaganda via cartoons preaching detestation and disdain for all things Israel— the Jews and their monikers for them the Little Satan—and the Big Satan—the United States and the target that ultimately must fall in their ideology of mayhem, maiming, massacre, and murder.

The United States' foundation upon Judeo and Christian precepts will always remain abhorrent to them. Any attempts at outreach and for dealings toward coexistence are outright rejected. There can be only one resolution, and that is that an Islamic caliphate span the entire globe and all peoples be under their oppressive thumb. A tenuous peace is unacceptable and could never be allowed to continue to flourish in their never-ending march against Western personal and individual freedoms. They want all to live a structured, by them of course, life of service to a dictatorial system that controls everyone's every moment and demands obedience to them, not God, ordained as unescapable and undeniable as *their truth*, and they are unshakable in that belief.

Benjamin Franklin famously stated: "They who can give up essential liberty to obtain a little temporary safety, deserve neither liberty nor safety," and human nature has become such that many accept the definition of peace as only the absence of immediate or sustained violence. Once introduced to fear, many will accept many concessions for a perceived sense of continued quiet.

GIJIAS feel no such compulsion to hold any amount of time of absence from violence. In fact, the opposite is true. You cannot instill or induce much fear in a group of radicals who believe they are given a form of extra credit in the form of martyrdom if they are killed in the act to slaughter infidels. They welcome their death under such conditions. There is little opportunity to reason with such a divergent mind-set.

Those thoughts kept occupying Marten's mind, but at that moment he knew he had to push those thoughts a bit deeper down to be able to focus on getting them organized sensibly and, hopefully, in compelling fashion into his manuscript. It was the time for Marten to put ink to paper and fingers to keyboard so that words would flow onto the digital page of his official manuscript to be ready for submission to a publisher. It was time to convey that surrender is not in our enemy's vocabulary, and that we shall only maintain any modicum of peace via Ronald Reagan's "peace through strength" mantra, and the assurance that we will use superior fire-power and technology to keep the enemy preoccupied with trying to remain hidden so as to avoid their fate and therefore have little to no time in order to plot against us.

Marten settled in at his desk. It had been several years since the idea of putting together a manuscript that outlined terrorist events across the United States, and how they were related with terrorist attacks and plots abroad, now at the forefront of Marten's mind. The added prestige and recognition that would come with the book's publication, Hope and Marten yearned, would allow Marten to take a position of editor-in-chief of a more rural area newspaper and allow them to move where the threats of violence, either via terrorism or general crime, were reduced, but he knew never negated entirely, and their daughters' safety more secure. A better environment—not just away from the violence, but to better schools for the children—was a major motivator. Hope spent so much time, part-time home-schooling, countering the indoctrination the kids mostly received during their traditional daily barrage beyond the basics of reading, writing, arithmetic in the public schools rather than education. She spent hours filling in the blanks, left by politically controlled and manipulated enclaves, of all the history and facts left out in order to mold kids to think a certain way rather than how to think for themselves based upon factual, contextual, history from all antiquity.

Marten tentatively adopted a working title of *Terrorist Tracks* or possibly *Terrorist Calendar* for his project. The title at this stage, though, was moot. Until there was a book to be concerned about adopting a title for, a title provided little use except for providing an implication for what the document's focus was to include.

The *Terrorist Tracks* concept allowed Marten an emphasis and attention to both tracing, tracking, trailing, the terrorists as people themselves, their motivations—often ill-defined protestations as abject hatred for all who do not bow to these Islamist fundamentalists, as well as their actions and presentation of how many of such assaults were upon passenger rail, track systems. Such vehicles once set in motion became enclosed tombs, full of victims they could slaughter by physical battering within or via a derailment stratagem.

Marten had already gathered some files containing information regarding the major successful terrorist attacks and some data on other high-profile events that were thwarted by the authorities. He also intended to include significant dates from the Muslim religious calendar, hence one of the potential titles, *Terrorist Calendar*, and key dates associated with anniversaries of prior attacks and attempts that the terrorists would most likely retarget. They had previous single-mindedly adhered to such meaningful dates, often to the detriment of their own plot.

He planned on breaking the book into chapters that addressed each event separately and to provide additional sections to discuss the potential root causes and motivations behind the various groups that are responsible for each of the actions, and where possible exposing the folly of their twisted logic justifications.

One such, copy-cat style of previous actions abroad—mugging normalcy and the moral "live and let live" philosophy—was to hit rural America to send the message that no one anywhere in the United States was safe or immune from having their life suddenly, viciously taken from them – literally could be coming soon, to a location near you.

The section of railway track between Tulsa and Sand Springs, Oklahoma, was a federally controlled railway line for connecting several private rail firms. Over the course of thirty years there had been near hits and misses with automobiles and trucks crossing the tracks, with almost weekly events where an approaching vehicle does not respond to the warnings and train's horns as motorists make an effort to beat the train through the crossing. Actual collisions had occurred at least ten times but had not resulted in death or major injury. Though one incident had resulted in a piece of rail breaking after being hit by an unidentified vehicle.

Hearings were held in Washington, DC, in May 2000 as a broader investigation to rail safety and concerns across all America, and Marten was able to glean information via the depositions conducted as a result of both the local and federal investigations of the Tulsa derailment.

In September 1999 an occurrence of track misalignment transpired that could have caused a serious derailment at that time had the two-inch expansion of the track width not been identified and corrected. A similar incident resulted in track integrity being degraded and requiring realignment when a motorhome was stuck on the track in the summer of 2011. The most serious concern was for the many hazardous materials tanker cars that made their way across these lines.

Many events had occurred regarding the line that was involved in the freight derailment Marten was focusing on. The likelihood that there was any actual terrorist involvement in this case was slim, but the pattern—given threats made and attempts made in even Asia against the Chinese people due to the oppression and the forced encampment of the Uyghurs, as well as so many previous rail attacks across Europe—warranted a good faith review of the materials. These were unintended mishaps, what damage might occur from a concerted attempt to derail a train cause?

It appeared to Marten that this was a case of the system at work, albeit slowly. Many individuals were working at closing crossings along the track in order to improve the integrity of the line and to prevent just another such accidental catastrophe. Further, it was evident that the degree of preparedness of the state and local officials had prevented the incident from becoming a nightmare of terrorist attack proportions, at least until now. The endless numbers of exposed, unguarded, track easily accessible to tampering, however, made them a much simpler target, and the GIJIAS may be looking for quick and easy high-injury, and potentially deaths, targets to get them back on the scoreboard so to speak.

In addition, from what Marten could recall the information was, as he was reviewing the file, that even if some of the particular crossings in question would have been closed, the chances of the accident occurring would not have been reduced as the traffic from those crossings would have just become funneled through other intersections, creating an even greater, more focused choke point for potential hits not just with the trains but with motorists stuck at the gates waiting to cross.

Of most concern was the JFK Boulevard crossing, though its closure would greatly increase traffic flow levels at the crossovers on either side. The very same vulnerabilities would have existed; they would have simply been redistributed. Time to study the amount of traffic at the in-question passages was needed, as well as time to perform any potentially perceived improvements in the other crossings.

The fact would always remain that a full inspection of every inch of railway, each and every day, and every train, could never become a realistic undertaking and viable possibility of train operations within the United States nor any other nation for that matter. The one hundred forty-one thousand miles of railway across the US could never be assured to be completely safe.

Improving the safety of the tracks was only one factor. Increasing the well-being of the tracks by reducing the number of points at which potential accidental damages increased the risk of properties abutting the throughway was another. Emergency vehicles, given absence of viaducts, would be required to reroute to alternate passages. Often local residents would try to fight closures in order to preserve their own convenience to cross the rails.

It would appear, given the lack of even any anecdotal evidence, no one claiming responsibility or physical clues suggesting purposeful damages of the track, advocated the fault lay with residents and politicians unwilling to sacrifice any opportunisms for the sake of shelter against harm. Then again, a variation of Franklin comes to play, do those willing to sacrifice freedom of movement for security, deserve either?

Marten had noticed an interesting pattern in the data, that there is a disproportionate amount of train-related mishaps in the state of Illinois. Negligence upon the part of local, state, federal, or combination of all, begged an answer. Why more so Illinois over the other forty-nine states?

Despite the general sturdiness and reliability of rails, Marten still had plenty of records to review of other locales incidents. In Gary, Indiana, in 1993, two trains collided causing seven fatalities, and many were injured; in 1995 in Fox River Grove, Illinois, a train struck a school bus that did not clear the tracks; in 1996, a passenger train accident in Silver Spring, Maryland, resulted in eleven fatalities; in 1997, following the fatal Maryland commuter train mishap, the

National Transportation and Safety Board recommended that voice recorders similar to those required for airliners—the infamous black boxes—be included on, at least, passenger rail trains. That was just a few of the chronicles in his pile of printed research from the 1990s. No decade subsequent to that one escaped some form of rail calamity. Rail is indeed safe in comparison to roadways, but certainly it could and would never be foolproof from occasional and varying degrees of catastrophe.

While the forces on either side of the issue worked to serve their own best interests, the seeds of a tragedy were sown. In the case of the JFK Tulsa crossing a track limit of ten miles an hour was in place in order to minimize car and train collisions, as well as prevent trains from toppling off the curved track leading up to it due to higher speeds probabilities.

Sadly, that fateful day in September 1999, no precautions mattered, and the pieces fell into place to wreak havoc on the neighboring community. A train had successfully navigated the curve and crossing just hours before. But that was then, this was not.

Chemical transport is a fact of life and will remain such as too so many who oppose pipelines despite there being more than two and a half million miles of it, with very few "incidents" to point to. We use so many, for varying reasons, and these chemicals must be transported from locale to locale one way or another—if not by rail, then by trucks, more precariously, over surface roads. Other than extreme track record of pipelines being reliable and benign, rail posed one of the more innocuous modes of transport.

A driver suffered a disruption of normal heart operation, and with the absence of other vehicles on his side of the crossing, he sped unobstructed into the crossing, slammed through the gate, and wedged under a chemical car of the currently passing train. The force leaned the chemical car, and the wedged vehicle didn't afford it the ability to sway back like in the occasional high winds or natural lean from a turn, and even with the low speed of the train a wheel slipped the confines of its guiding tracks.

Again, safeguards exist, railcars are inspected. Older cars potentially no longer viable to assure protections are removed from the fleet. This one, whose life expectancy should have removed it from operation, slipped past the inspector's eye, and the hatch gave way as the railcar slid onto its side. Chemicals spewed forth as the train engaged its brakes. These large and heavy means of transport do not stop quickly.

All the norms that would typically prevent further danger than just the need for a cleanup didn't exist that day. The dryness of the brush from sparks ignited. Slowly, but far too fast for the right emergency equipment to handle a chemical fire to respond to the scene, allowed for the chemical to combust. Then, of course, not only did fire become a great concern, but so too did toxic fumes as they began to billow and, abetted by the winds, head toward the housing development nearby. Firefighting combined with a need for neighborhood evacuation compounded the local responders' problems.

As great American heroes, first responders, as they do daily, rushed to the scene. The fire crews, donned in their breathing aid gear, began to foam the chemical induced flames. The local sheriff agency, which was first on scene, began to evacuate drivers on the other side of the crossing, reverse 911 emergency services—as 911 allows citizens to reach their local emergency services, reverse 911 allows local emergency services to make automated prerecorded informational message delivery to area citizens—engaged and calls attempted to reach those in the homes needing rescue themselves. Additional police, fire units, and emergency medical technicians arrived to expand the perimeter and even had to call in more help from the surrounding communities to launch a door-to-door notification that the residences needed to temporarily relinquish occupancy of their dwellings.

That day was one thing. Later, like with the first responders and volunteers at ground zero on 9/11, came the fume-related lung damage and breathing issues. It's a reminder that the supposed conclusion of a tragedy might be misleading. Days, weeks, months, sometimes years after the seeds have been sown other effects that would impact those nearby rear their ugly heads.

5

FLASHBACK

NO WEAPON THAT IS FORMED AGAINST THEE
SHALL EVER PROSPER.

—Isaiah 54:17

"Move! Move! Move!"

"Where's that coming from?"

"Where's our air support?" a third voice chimed in.

"Inbound, sir!" Another soldier yelled.

"Damn it, hurry up. Move! Move! Move!"

"What are you waitin' on? Fire back moron."

"At what?"

"You see the goddamn tracers don't ya?"

Marten recalled reading the account of the Gulf War veteran's version of his torment. Over and over his nightmare revisited him. The difference, Marten thought, that poor soul, unlike his fictitious dreams, actually lived it in real life. The horror, just the knowledge of what those first-hand experiences were doing to fellow caring individuals caught in life-and-death struggles, was enough, in part, to fuel his empathetic night terrors.

Post-Traumatic Stress Disorder, previously clinically diagnosed as shell shock from back to the First World War days. A stigma existed in previous generations of Korean and Vietnam flashbacks. Knowing, however, how the mind is reacting is a far cry from being able to treat the neurological torture. How? Why?

The effect that his friend Tim suffered on a daily basis was profound, on not just him but on loved ones around him. A camping excursion just a few years prior exposed Marten to the misery his comrade endures almost nightly, sometimes more than one occurrence would surface. During a seemingly blissful sleep, Tim sprang to life. Bouncing up onto his hands and knees, like a man possessed, searching feverishly for a lost . . . something! Rotating in place, patting the ground, revolving left, gyrating right, and as quickly and inexplicably as the actions started, they ceased. Tim would often be none the wiser for the ordeal. That is, until morning. The number of instances directly correlating to the day's lethargy episodes due to his sleep having been sporadic.

Tim, here-to-fore, had not even been aware of these episodes. No one pinpointed his daylight hour nap requirements with the nighttime intrusions. No doctor had bothered to conduct a sleep study; they just treated his memory loss as if it were an isolated concern as opposed to the warning sign and indication of a much greater and deeper problem.

Tim was now trying to address the problem via his Veteran Affairs benefits and VA Hospital, but relief was not likely anywhere near. Being unmarried and otherwise currently unattached, Tim had to rely on Marten and his other friends to convince him he was not alone. It was not weak to reach out for help, beyond the doctors, to join a support group, they told him.

Marten's family had known the pains of war before his acquaintance and subsequent friendship with Tim. In fact, Tim seemed to be, despite his situation, somewhat fortunate since his mental trespasses occurred only during his sleep, and he hadn't even been waking from them to deal with the trauma in a conscious state. Tim did not have to endure endless intrusions into his day-to-day life.

Some of Marten's family members had to suffer bouts of his continual incursions of memories throughout the day—the uncontrolled spasms of synaptic recollections of horrific days and events best left buried deep within the recesses of the mind. Yet, there they were, catapulted to the fore—not just a bad memory, not a fiction like Marten's nightmares, but complete and all-encompassing here and now, real time, current happenings.

For those family members, driving a car was out of the question. Their episodes could be triggered at any given moment and required someone to take control to bring them back to reality and overcome the false impression that they were back in the thick of their previous, hazardous state of affairs—back in the life-and-death struggle.

The Korean and Vietnam conflicts were of another time and place. The landscape, battlefields, and terrain were much more foreign than today's fronts. Granted, jungle warfare had been a part of the Second World War combat zones, the advent of refined Guerilla tactics, the improved, yet still limited, weaponry of the time, and the hostile political climate tainted the specter of those conflicts.

The kamikaze mindset of not only uniformed soldier combatants, in those wars the entire populace were enemies— even more so terrorists—had zero regard for the rules of war or the Geneva convention. Anyone and everyone were a potential enemy or considered a valid target, waiting patiently and quietly to lull us into a false sense of security before striking; and on our side anyone and everyone was a considered very immoral by even their own religious texts commandments, a legitimate mark.

The battle paradigm in those wars that forced our soldiers to defend themselves against women and children, against all their notions of humanity, destroyed the fragile innocent psyche. Modern GIJIAS purposefully, willfully, and with much malice caused mental wounds upon Western cultures' innocent, otherwise non-combatant, general populace.

That anyone treated the soldiers of the First or Second World War who'd suffered these horrors and utter inhumanity as simply shell-shock victims today seems an insane notion. We failed those heroes who needed our compassion, support, and comforting rather than being treated as if they were suffering a form of insanity.

In the Korean and Vietnam conflicts death loomed around every corner, in every dwelling, behind any tree. At any moment a homicidal mother or distraught child, who'd been given something to "take to an American," potentially even without family advice and consent, waited to take life. This was the soldiers' reality, a never-ending nightmarish state never before conceived even by the horror noir freaks of Hollywood.

There were walkways with false floors to entrap unsuspecting Joes into pits with poisonous bungee sticks. Strands of vines carefully placed to pull a grenade pin when unsuspectingly tugged upon from a Joe passing through. Strategically placed barriers were set up to guide groups of soldiers down a path directly into the killing zone of a machine gun pit.

The foreign sights, sounds, smells, and tastes relentlessly reminded the soldiers that this was nothing whatsoever like home. The endless buzzing of crickets, frogs, mosquitos, flies, and every other imaginable pest penetrated the quiet, preventing them from hearing a tell-tale sound of an enemy troop who may be lying in wait nearby. The sudden bursts of tracers and bullets pounding in every direction and relentless mortar fire and return fire in every direction in the hopes that engagement could be made accidentally through this haphazard manic self-defense gesture added to the chaos.

Everyone prayed silently, begging God or anyone that would listen, don't let anyone be hit, at least not seriously hurt by such. A seriously wounded soldier would mean they would be pinned down as they would have to try and create a plan to hold ground, layout an escape path, and somehow get to an evacuation clearing. There simply were no options, if you became engaged, you had to completely destroy the enemy's position. They must all be destroyed or otherwise incapacitated, or you would remain pinned down until they could bring in reinforcements to encircle your troop and slaughter you all. The name of the game was numbers, who could sufficiently locate, pin, and bring in additional overwhelming firepower to destroy all opposition the winner of any given battle.

No one could be left standing. Any enemy combatant left wounded would be back in short order to fight again another day. Soldiers who lost an arm didn't go home, these jungles were their homes. They would be propped up with a weapon in a blind with the sole duty of killing as many American GIs as possible before being killed himself.

Their love and devotion to Marxist or fascist creeds and hate toward dirty capitalists in their minds, although the free market, more appropriately called, system by which more have been lifted from poverty and given freedoms and peace than any other, overcame any regard for themselves or even self-preservation normally associated with humans. Preservation of their current land and expansionism of communism or fascism was their only driving force.

Mankind's folly as to a war being able to be fought within considered acceptable norm's, was beyond an insane notion. You cannot fight a war with a set of hard-and-fast rules that your enemy promptly disregards or further uses to their advantage in the killing fields.

White flags of surrender or truce were often simply rouses to gain a better proximity for an attack. Death was the only thing that would stop the incensed, zombie-like guerrilla fighters, no matter the age of the combatant. Where men could not tread, Napalm had to lead the way. Going around was just another trap that had been laid.

These wars, as to some extents are all wars, are means of attrition and forcefully imposing one's will upon others. The slow destruction of the enemy's strongholds, the wearing away of the enemy's supply lines, and the erosion of their very will to fight, did little against a people whose desire to live in peace and coexistence just didn't exist in their DNA.

Because of the inadequate parsing of territories following the Second World War, subsequent wars have become more complicated. Countries were left in flux by the troop movements after the official end of the war. Peace treaty ink was no sooner dry when older latent hostilities caused by arbitrarily post-war drawn lines on a map flared up.

Upon the end of the Second World War, France immediately increased their troop levels in Vietnam and continued the cause of liberating the people against the communists, that were convenient temporary allies only a few years earlier. After years of fighting remained at a stale mate, new advances in weaponry did not provide any breakthroughs required to tip the conflict in Frances's favor. After years of going it alone, despite alliances with the United Kingdom and United States who did not engage under NATO cooperation treaty, the French began to pull out.

The United States, concerned about a reignition of Second World War hostilities, secretly prepared to fill the void the French troops were leaving. Hindsight, as they say, is always 20/20. How might things have been different if the UK and the USA entered the fight alongside the French, seeking to free the people from the existential threat George Patton had warned about, but battle-weary nations just wanted to bury their heads back into the sand and hope that minor conflicts, that could have set dormant for another century, and in many cases did, would not explode to greater and broader conflict. The rest of the world could burn so long as those battle-weary nations could maintain their perceived sense of armistice and harmony. For some war-weary nations, only if the enemy marched upon their shores would they be shaken to engage again to stabilize the world and fight for people to be free.

No, it was fine by many, that "those people" we once fought on behalf of be allowed to be imprisoned behind the Iron-curtain, controlled by the communists who were guilty of slaughtering so many in the name of conformity, or because they are not the right sort of people, also had engaged in.

For some reason people are unable to make the connection that the same issue of abrasion, erosion, gnawing away at our rights today. The current enemies of freedom are more than happy to engage us in a long battle, knowing many in Western cultures are all about instant gratification with little regard for the future. The tyrants—whether they be communists, fascists, or GIJIAS—believe they shall be victorious in time and don't care how long it will take until their final goal of destroying infidels, as they define everyone that is not them, all across the globe. They do not suffer the same disease of instant gratification that those who love peace have been afflicted with. Those who desire peace, rightfully so, do not wish to engage in war. War is undesirable to freedom and peace-loving peoples and is something to be avoided. In the minds of some, war, even when required to defend oneself, when in their own best interest, is opposed. Whereas our enemies see war as a must and a calling to enslave their neighboring nations and peoples.

Fundamentalists, political or religious, view war differently. They view war like the GIJIAS view their Jihad, as a necessity in which they embrace. They offer no quodlibet, only dictation of caitiff beliefs. This mentality will not change. Like the fascists of the Second World War, these "believers" will not be stopped until we are all captured and made their slaves or killed. This dogma must be forced into submission and kept in check by our own use of brute force or when possible economic counter-balance. The unfortunate truth is that it may require worldwide battles in each and every corner of the planet, such as those that were required to defeat Nazi-ism.

We can guess which nations will likely side with those looking to destroy freedom-loving peoples, as temporary allies in hopes that, as the saying goes, the monster may be too tired to then even desire to eat them last. The old adage the enemy of my enemy is my friend is clearly false. They may be a useful ally today, but be warned we will likely have to engage them another day—just as was the case with Russia, which expanded into an evil Soviet Union, beyond the Second World War. To defeat a greater evil, we temporarily teamed up with our enemy, which then become the new global threat to humanity and freedom.

Likewise, reports in the *New York Times* and other such publications purported that a war in Iraq to overthrow Saddam had increased the recruitment of fundamentalist fighters allied against the United States. These media outlets ignored the fact that no matter what the United States does, there will be propaganda enticing available recruits through targeted messaging and radical teachings from the Quran by such people as Usama bin Laden and his ilk. Indeed, when Obama pulled all troops out of Iraq rather than leaving quick reaction forces in theater, ISIS, also known as ISIL, filled the void as so many warned would occur.

Sadly, many thought that when the US Navy Seals killed Usama, the so-called War on Terror would conclude. The death of a leader will line up additional human drones for the cause, in and of itself. Therefore, should we avoid targeting the al Qaeda or ISIL/ISIS leaders because it would inflame and incite some to join their ranks?

As ridiculous as this Chamberlainesque policy has proven over and over, there are some that feel this type of appeasement is required in order to reduce the justification of those predisposed toward hating non-Muslim's or vice versa.

If the United States had not invaded Iraq—which incidentally the Iraqi Liberation Act signed by Bill Clinton made it US policy that, at some point, the US would have to remove Saddam—then Saddam were still running Iraq today. And the most fanatical fundamentalists, desirous of their own lust for power, would still be manipulating young men to foment hatreds toward Western civilization.

If the United States had not invaded Afghanistan, and to a lessor-extent Iraq, then the Left would argue that the United Sates is weak a morally bankrupt, not that the USA wished to avoid conflict, as was the case when Bill Clinton cut-and-ran from Somalia. Conversely, the Left pushes the false narrative that since the USA had chosen to take an offensive initiative by placing the battlefields within the Middle East and Asia, from where the majority of the fundamentalist recruits are courted, as well as where the greatest numbers of the terrorists training camps are located, that somehow makes the United States an evil imperialistic empire looking to oppress all of Islam. There will never be a lack of volunteers, in one shape or form, until absolute defeat of the infidels. The weak minded are always willing to step forward for the cause until the very notion of why they should fight is perceived as futile. There will always remain endless justifications in the minds, foreign or domestic, that hate America.

The war of words, the battle for hearts and minds, of which many speak is an unwinnable notion because the arguments will just be warped to fit the current situation and create propaganda false-narratives. Every time nations have tried to conciliate those whose true aim is oppression and destruction of a race or other classification of people; the result has been only an increased level of death and demolition has occurred when the battle is enjoined.

6

TOKYO, JAPAN

WE THEN, AS WORKERS, TOGETHER WITH [GOD].

—2 Corinthians 6:1

*T*errorism based on twisted religious fanaticism is not limited to just one part of the earth. Japan has its share of extremists acting in furtherance of their faith and calls for the Apocalypse. Also, Japan has more than its fair share of rail related incidents, some accidental and some acts of terrorism.

It was a cool, misty Monday morning one spring as Tokyo began its hectic workweek. From their base in Kamiku Isshiki, at the base of Mount Fuji, members of the AUM Shinrikyo—the Supreme Truth, identified by many as an apocalyptic religious sect or doomsday cult—made the final preparations for their assault.

For whatever reason, there seemed to be a lot of doomsday cults, as they most often are referred to, during the turn of the millennium. They, however, did not engage in mayhem and manslaughter in the hopes of ushering in Armageddon. The prevalence of groups believing that the end times are at hand seemed at an all-time high in the decade prior to the close of the second millennium and surged even more at the close of 2012, as some claimed the Mayan's predicted that was the end of time—even though that was not what the Mayan calendar of ever repeating cycles denoted at all.

AUM Shinrikyo, one of the largest doomsday cults in Asia had its headquarters at the base of Mount Fuji. They existed well beyond Tokyo, or even Japan, with offices in Russia, the United States, and many other locations throughout the globe. That is, until they engaged in attempted mass murder and investigators looked into its terrorist roots and operations all over the globe and shutdown most locations.

On that cool Monday morning, five, two-man squads, were dispatched to their predetermined locations. Their plan, not completely unique, in fact most terrorist outbreaks are copy-cat, or slight variations on a previous guideline, was to release poisonous gases into the Tokyo subway. They quietly blended in with the commuters in the subway system. Carefully trying to not call attention to themselves, they placed their crude detonation devices into place as they intermingled amongst the crowds. Their intent was to wait for larger crowds and to escape the kill zone just before detonating them for maximum damage.

Their devices were far more diabolical than the Boston Marathon Bombers improvised explosive devices, which contained small ball bearings and nails to try and maximize their attempts to disable as many as possible and potentially cause mass-casualties as they might bleed-out awaiting rescue services savior. The Supreme Truth, however, was going for maximum kill from the start. Through underground dealings, they managed to acquire poison gas that would spread far greater distances than ball bearings, nails, glass, and the like. In fact, in such bouts some victims could, would, and do, shield potential victims from being struck. Human-shields, much like Islamic terrorists among the Gaza-strip and other warzones around Israel use in another sense. Human-shields meant to deter retaliation against them, as innocent women and children would be gathered and put out front to protect the terrorists. They know any retaliations resulting in collateral deaths, and images of slaughtered women and children, would turn loving, caring nations against the enemies of these fanatics, who purposefully target innocents. They want mass collateral killing of innocents among the wreckage of surrounding infrastructure. Damaged infrastructure makes an obstacle against first responders trying to get save victims.

Many governments, like Iran and Syria, that have a long history of terrorism, have had chemical agents. Iran and Iraq used nerve agents on each other during their war. Those two nations made it clear they were fine with using such weapons the Geneva convention had hoped to eliminate after the destructive nature of nerve gases was exposed during the First World War.

Syria used them against their own citizens during their civil war. Assad contends they were not used by his forces, or by his order, but by others hoping to cast aspersions upon his regime. The Syrian head-of-state continues to insist they were false-flag operations, to discredit his administration. These accusations cannot certainly ever be truly investigated until a peace could be obtained between the warring factions, which at the time of Marten's book release would most likely still be ongoing.

Who has these chemicals? Who would sell or gift them to terrorist organizations? To whom actually would either provide to spread mayhem or just sell for profit such "Weapons of Mass Destruction?" That is a whole other issue that could be fodder for many fictional books or films.

One of Marten's favorites movies, *Sum of all Fears*, is based on a novel by Tom Clancy, one of his favorite authors. In it someone provided a terrorist enriched uranium. The terrorist planned bombing of a US city in the hopes of blaming Russia in order to drive Western nations into engagement against Eastern forces and usher in a third world war.

That was not the motivations of the AUM Shinrikyo. They just wanted to cause mayhem and murder to draw attention to their message that we were in the end times. Not unlike the motivations of the Twelvers in Iran, the AUM Shinrikyo believed it was their duty to help usher in the apocalypse.

Just like the terrorists in Gaza, the AUM Shinrikyo wanted to create as much infrastructure damage to potentially bury their targets so rescuers would have to spend precious seconds, minutes, and, in some cases, hours trying to get to those needing their services and thus maximize the carnage. They carried the liquid form Cyanide gases in inconspicuous plastic soft drink containers. They even reassigned several inert agents that would aerosolize and help carry the deadly poisonous aspects of the lethal gases. The complexity of the agents was specifically, and diabolically, designed to obscure its sources and complicate the ability to both combat the agents once released and confound the capacity to trace the origins as law enforcement investigative matters.

The presence of multiple chemical agents would confuse the ability to treat the afflicted. By releasing vapors and fumes from numerous types of chemicals the symptoms would vary causing first responders and medical personnel to be thrown into a massively chaotic situation in which they would be disoriented by the divergent poison indicators and the attackers hoped first responders would find it impossible to determine the proper treatments amongst the various wounded and dying.

Those exposed at the same site would have different symptoms based on the toxins that were released. The delay this would, as medical teams try to determine a treatment, lead to additional deaths; as treatment uncertainty delayed suppression, and recovery from, the gas, and providing added time for the chemical to perform its evil intent.

The terrorists rely on people seemingly settling into a notion that were infrequent due to the complexity of past attacks and thus let their guard down. However, perception and reality were not always in sync. By planning fewer complex attacks, they would now happen more frequently and could come in spurts all around the world.

Anyone sympathetic to the terrorists causes, could now just jump into a large vehicle and mow down unsuspecting peoples like happened in the Christmas of 2021 attacks in Wisconsin. Assaults with high-powered rifles could easily be coordinated and enacted in short order, like the attempted attack on a train to Paris dramatized in the Clint Eastwood film *The 15:17 to Paris*, which is another favorite film of Marten's, based on the 2016 autobiography *The 15:17 to Paris: The True Story of a Terrorist, a Train, and Three American Heroes*, or the Beltway snipers' assaults

The number of domestic and foreign terrorist groups was rapidly increasing throughout the 1990s and early 2000s. The horrific scale of 9/11 left so many in awe, and for some time subsequent assaults obviously were lower in scale and therefore not as newsworthy all across the globe, thereby giving the perception to many that terrorism was waning. Instead, the scale and scope of attacks were just downgraded, as such large-scale attacks would clearly take a vast amount of planning that would more likely be exposed post-9/11 by agencies being more proactive in prevention than just reactive to identify criminals to put in prison. For a while a post-9/11 major focus was to capture non-declared enemy combatants for placement at GITMO to try and garner information not to just prosecute past events but intercept ongoing operations and potential attacks in the works for the shorter and longer terms.

Only the major assaults, like the Tokyo subway gassing, were covered worldwide. Some terrorist attacks, due to political correctness and the newer growing WOKEism meant to suppress "conspiracies," were kept off national or global media networks. Also, some decisions to not report large attacks because doing so was seen as just giving terrorists partially what they wanted: a larger audience being terrified and paranoid. Even though it was indeed true that an incident could happen at any time in any place. As targets became more secured and harder to hit, soft targets inevitably would become the new ways and places to strike.

Since smaller scale attacks were still being widely reported still on local levels, that meant more successful actions were able to take place and more people were informed of them, which emboldened the terrorists, or those sympathetic to their causes. Individuals felt they could join the GIJIAS without needing to be part of an official cell. They could go out on their own and kill in the name of whoever. The side effect of less reporting of larger attacks, however, also heartened the cultists as they then felt they were immune from capture and disruption.

A sense of complacency tends to settle in after just a few weeks after heightened awareness, after people have a basic remembrance of the general vulnerability of free societies to those who would seek to do them harm. Terrorists simply wait out the initial increase in attentiveness, consciousness, and responsiveness, before undertaking their next devasting deed. In the meantime, they were free to continue to conspire, plan, and prepare—or just engage elsewhere.

The hustle-and-bustle grew on that normal Monday morning, March 20, 1995. Hayashi placed a jug and a second container down onto the floor of the front subway car of the southwest bound Chiyoda line. Hayashi, after making sure his escape path was clear, used his umbrella to begin the interactions of the chemicals within the container, allowing the deadly poisons to convert from liquid form into the highly toxic gaseous from. He then pierced the jug to discharge its lethal vapors into the poorly ventilated subway station. Meanwhile, his cohorts were prepared to do the same, around about the same time. They worked in two-person teams to be able to maximize carnage on the one hand, while allowing for them to be able to coordinate an exit.

The same sights, sounds, and smells played out at four locations encompassing greater Tokyo, all amidst the subway line connections that pass through the Japanese government's power base enclaves of Kasumigaseki and Natatacho. After the fact, it was clear to investigators that the main target of these attacks was Japanese officials' family members, if not some of the Japanese government office holders themselves.

The same scenes played out at several locations across Tokyo. People lay on the ground gasping for air, blood streamed from their noses and mouths. Others who were close to the blasts were disabled and therefore unable to get away from the expanding toxic gases zone. Still others were knocked down and trampled under-feet as they tried to escape only to be left to succumb to the noxious fumes designed to kill them.

While the potency of the cyanide gases was increased by the addition of other compounds, none was as potent as weapons grade cyanide agent if it had been acquired for use or a military delivery mechanism employed. In that respect, the tragedy unfolding would have been greatly underrated.

Thousands of casualties would have occurred had just a fraction of the amount of that gas been deployed in the enclosed subway area and left to work its airborne effects, out and onto the surrounding street level. As it was thousands were injured but only thirteen deaths were attributed to the terror strike.

This attack provided an ominous foreboding of potential attacks, and proof that a dirty bomb, just not of radioactive nature this outing, was well within the reach and ability of today's terrorists. Marten knew he had to impress upon his readers, more than once, of copycat attacks.

The terrorist tracks of the confined station actually worked against the killers, in this incident, but not necessarily so of later copy-cat style acts. The other 'terrorist tracks' aspect; revelations as to their plotting, planning, and actual implementation; as would be defined in Marten's book, regarding the incident took months to reveal.

Arrest warrants for murder were eventually issued against AUM leader Shoko Asahara and upwards of four Supreme Truth cult followers. Yoshihiro Inoue, twenty-five-year-old karate expert who was identified as the groups intelligence chief, was also insnared in the dragnet. He was charged with leading the five two-person crews.

Inoue was a high-value target as he was suspected as being a part of additional plots outside of AUM. Getting Inoue behind bars was considered a major blow against the cult and possibly prevented other attacks the rest of the year from occurring around Tokyo.

Respiratory predicaments arose around other parts of Tokyo. Reports of mysterious fumes elsewhere caused concern. As many as twenty people were affected in one case. While three people were hospitalized, they were quickly listed in satisfactory condition. No one was arrested for that incident, nor were they ever to officially identify the substance or the source.

The train attack remains as the most serious attack on Japanese soil since the conclusion of the Second World War, with more than six thousand persons injured and fifty-five hundred persons requiring hospitalization. The Supreme Truth, in just one attack, seemed to be able to inflict more impairment in terms of actual damage to the Japanese psyche than by the pro-communist Japanese Red Army militant group in the 1970s and 1980s.

The AUM Shinrikyo sect contended that the Japanese government staged the subway attacks and attributed them to the religious group as a ploy and cover to rally public opinion against it in a bid to alienate, if not, eliminate, the group. That is the same tactic many terrorists use; they try to deflect blame or appear as victims themselves. It's the familiar false-flag conspiracy theme. It seems that "conspiracy theory" propagandists are pretty much the same the world over. Clearly, they read each other's manifestos and imitate each other's styles and methodologies.

Later, thirty balloons landed in a three-hundred-twenty-mile area south of Tokyo. It was reported small tubes were attached to each of the balloons. No official release was made as to what substance the tubes may have contained, or if they were just meant to add to the mayhem and disrupt any calm Tokyo had hoped would come. Fears of terrorism were piqued a decade later when a commuter train derailed and crashed into a residential building in Amagasaki, Japan. That incident killed more than sixty people. The cause of the Amagasaki mishap, a few hundred kilometers west of Tokyo, was later deemed human error. The relief felt over an incident being an accident was little consolation and another rail attack could indeed transpire again.

7

"LOVE VS FAKE HATE"

AND NOW ABIDE FAITH, HOPE, LOVE, THESE THREE;
BUT THE GREATEST OF THESE IS LOVE.

—1 Corinthians 13:13 NIV

Certainly, there are many people who hate, who have real hatred in their hearts and souls both as individuals and as parts of groups. There are also those, however, who have no compunction over pitting one group against another and create fake-hate claims; some might even go so far as to say mini "false-flag" operations in and of themselves, in order to sway public opinion to achieve political aims.

There will always be some degree of prejudice and possibly real hate from some to another based upon color of skin and other factors even within race and how people handle themselves, some regional variances, classes, or even religious differences. The bottom line though, is others trump up division for political gain the Saul Alinsky way: demonize your opponent by any means necessary, even if fabricated.

All that matters to some people is separation by color, class, or any means necessary, as a method to divide and conquer. Some people in the Democratic Party want to pit one distinctive 'Identity Politics' group, real or imagined, against another. For the modern fascists all that matters is power and control. Deflection, distraction, division, it's all a compulsory tactic to prevent any real and careful examination of their own failings. The fact that several of their party's platform planks are virtually identical to those in the Nationalsozialistische Deutsche Arbeiterpartei (Nazi Party) platform—including, but not limited to, the nationalization of healthcare. If you control a person's access to the means by which they can stay healthy or to receive aid when sick, you control the people. Even more so, the threat that medications could be withheld from loved ones, if you yourself do not comply with the tyrannical government – pretending to be so compassionate by offering you governmental, death-panels, measured care.

Saul Alinsky was a radical activist, rabble-rouser, and one of the first community activists in Chicago who wrote *Rules for Radicals*. One of Alinsky tactics was adopted by prior fascists too: tell big lies and repeat them until they are believed. Use intimidation, incite violence, and use supporters to engage in violence. We'd certainly seen that in 1930s Germany and Italy to help grab power and maintain control—just as we are seeing in the United States today by American fascists. The powerful elite may hide behind a twisted rhetoric, deflect and dodge honest debate, claim to be anti-fascists, but they are no different than the original tyrants themselves – which is also in part why American fascists do not allow actual history to be taught in government-controlled schools, otherwise the masses may learn from it.

Marten longed to be a feature columnist where he could engage in opinion. Instead, he settled for writing occasional online articles at the *Before It's News* site under a nom de plume. He was careful to adopt a far more casual writing style from that of his strait-laced one at work as part of his guise – fake name, honest opinions, derived from facts not feelings and what is effective over fake good intentions but policy fails of the modern fascists.

One such time a friend from a rival paper leaked to Marten a Letter to the Editor by Joe Bernhardt. The leaker knew the particular letter would interest Marten, and relate to his book topic in some respects. It was correspondence about the false claims of hate. Or, if not fake, clearly exaggerated that the new 'Woke' culture had elevated the degree of "Political Correctness" as a means of political end by keeping people distracted and focused on divisions rather than our likenesses and commonalities.

Joe Bernhardt's letter, a response to yard signs virtue signaling and glorifying the LGBT agenda and hating on his fellow Christians that were popping up on lawns throughout southeast Michigan.

Joe's letter read:

I bet when you ran your "attempt to be cute and clever" story on these "Neighbors Against HATE" signs, you thought there couldn't possibly be any push back. Well, you were so wrong — let's deal in reality rather than in false narratives and psychological projection you choose to allow to be printed.

1) How about love thru actual deeds NOT virtue signaling, fake woke, empty rhetoric (literal strawman), psychological projection slogans?

My response (handmade "love" sign) saying:

Real love by deeds vs fake anti-hate (strawman) virtue signaling!

When was the last time **you** gave a hungry stranger a meal?

When have **you** helped veterans in need?

When have **you** given to homeless shelters (plural)?

When did YOU last give to any charity at all?!?!?

2) What is this really about?

I am a Christian, and every Christian I know **has no hate in their hearts toward** anyone, not overtly nor covertly - PERIOD! Atheists or others with a secular agenda, away from our founding fathers' Judeo-Christian foundations intentions, must always twist, distort, spin, make **strawman** implications of our positions!

Is this yet another unfounded "**cry racism**" ploy? (Who founded the KKK? Who were the Confederate States run by? Who passed those Jim Crow **hate** Laws? Sadly, history is NOT TAUGHT but instead **spun** under the guise of social studies GUISE now-a-days!

Need we mention the Smollett and countless other **hoaxes**? **Who** is peddling **segregation yet again today** (black only dorms, graduations, etc.) on College Campuses today? And do we really have to bring up the division and hate being peddled by the Left through **critical race theory** (CRT); contrary to Martin Luther King Jr's Dream of individualism and content **of character;** being peddled in Schools (and spare us the LIES that it is not). You can change the -term- (what you call it, or even shy away from the CRT acronym) all you like, but we know it is still being pushed upon even grade schoolers.

Or is this about yet another LGBTQPxyz dodge (even excusing pedophiles, sexualization of children, peddling porn in grade schools, and even ignoring **Statutory-rape** laws, engaging in attempts to cover up BIOLOGICAL BOYS attacking girls in girls' restrooms)!? So WHERE are their companion "**Neighbors against sexual predators**" or "**Neighbors against criminals**" signs?!

A key point in your report was an inebriated buffoon (**individual**) involved (not their entire block with pitch-forks mob) but hey **let's project this onto everyone (all Christians) else** again to smear the group.

Despite this proving to be about the LGBTQ2+ agenda, it could clearly be applicable to the other leftist agendas of divisions through racist HATE HOAXES.

Why? Simple... They cannot have a real and honest discussion, SO CALL YOUR NEIGHBORS HATERS instead. SCREAM RACIST OR HOMOPHOBE and run away pretending they've won the argument they know they cannot win if held **honestly** (actually have any discussion at all)!

Words vs deeds, and what "religion" (and let me be clear it is NOT the entire religion or peoples of that "faith" but some EXTREMISTS within) is STILL STONING LGBTQ PEOPLE TO DEATH? OR THROWING THEM FROM BUILDINGS?!?! Where the real **hate** is they don't bother to speak about. Just ask Dr. Zuhdi Jasser (author of: A Battle for the Soul of Islam: An American Muslim Patriot's Fight to Save His Faith)! If I have to explain further, then you clearly are **clueless**, living under one of the rocks they would pelt you with.

Ask Dave Chappelle about **where real hate** resides. His THE CLOSER special spends 15 minutes on Daphne, his trans friend who committed suicide likely due to LGBTQ-ON-LGBTQ HATE. The special teaches EMPATHY, but they say that **he is transphobic** and try to get his special pulled from the air.

Add to the long list of folks you could have talked to in order to add **balance**. There is transgender **Blair White** and her prominent role in the **WALK AWAY FROM THE PARTY OF LIES, FAKE NEWS, DIVISION, HATE—the FASCICRATS Party**. There is the purposeful participation in Tom MacDonald's SNOWFLAKES video and key placement of Blair flipping the bird when Tom is talking about pathetical corruptness **pronouns** nonsense.

As Paul Harvey used to say: Now you know the rest of the story!

But, hey, wait, there's more. The next deflection: **Look another statue to tear down** and distort **history** completely out of context of not just our own nation but against the rest of the world.

I'm willing to bet your neighborhood is like mine. All the **BLACK LIVES MATTER** signs, except **mine**, which says **BLACK LIVES MATTER, BLUE LIVES MATTER, NOT EITHER/OR** (which was out all last year, all this year) that speak truth do not fit your liberal papers agenda and therefore you would never do a story about me and my friends and family having those signs, and will be out still next year, because I actually believe in my causes and not vacuous virtue signaling hypocrite/deceiver like them), but all theirs **are gone** because that cause was so last year. They LOST that argument. They were **exposed as hypocrites and deceivers and frauds**. They did not have any clue about who racist Margaret Sanger was. They did not know that she founded Planned Parenthood and why she targeted inner cities. They were exposed as **frauds** for not caring at all about the black **genocide** going on in the Planned Parenthood centers. They only cared about Black Lives that were **politically convenient** to the Democrats' "defund **the police**" rhetoric (which they've lost that aspect of the debate also as a survey shows that 4 out of 5 Black people want the same or more police protection). They lost that debate, so all those Signs are now **gone** — and onto the **next distraction, deflection, and dodge, the latest empty rhetoric slogan!**

(Below is the image of the sign I made from scratch, not some prefabricated, pre-purchased, mass-produced propaganda, strawman, virtue signaling, signs)

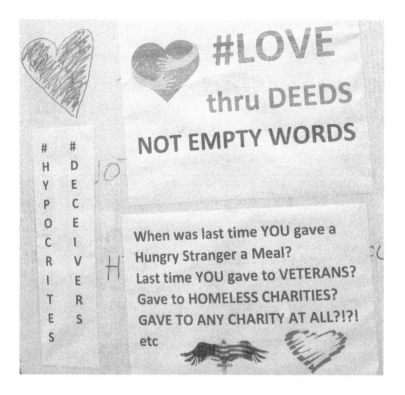

Marten absolutely agreed with the letter and the enclosed image Joe sent of his sign, though, it was clearly too long for any press outlet to ever publish, and they likely wouldn't take the time to edit it down to a brief summary of that letter authors points because it didn't fit their narrative. Marten decided the sentiments needed expanding, and the only way that could be done by him was to flesh it out at *Before It's News* under his nom-de-plume, where he was then free to provide opinion pieces of his own; free of any of his normal professional position constraints. He would include what his yard sign, including hashtags should someone copy it for social media use, would read in solidarity of Joe's sign image, if he were putting one on his lawn and then elaborated from there:

THEY "talk about HATE" (#hypocrites / #deceivers)

With their empty rhetoric "NEIGHBORS VS HATE" signs

Because #FASCICRATS are THE PARTY OF HATE

He thought better of indeed actually making the physical sign. He knew, as part of a newspaper operation and being old-school, that he needed to remain as neutral as possible, publicly, anything actually associated with his real name, his home, etc. Just speculating what his sign would say, would suffice. Sadly, so many print, radio, and television outlets today no longer even pretend to be neutral, and their story choices, how they are written, show that. **Opinion** laden pieces had become the entire process, not just limited to the editorial pages. As he wrote his piece, he made sure to included hashtags because it is not just for social media, but part of the overall manner in which Google and other search-engines grab keywords to categorize his piece so his article would be shared. This, however, was his chance to let loose his thoughts unrestrained, and his blog continued – about if he actually could put signs out on his front lawn:

That sign would be proudly displayed next to other signs denoting...

1) Protect Religious Freedom

2) Black Lives Matter, Blue Lives Matter, NOT EITHER/ OR

3) 9/11 Never Forget

4) VOTE BIBLICALLY

Given some uproar with comedian Dave Chappelle, he thought it best to start his blog process with a bit of bad humor to make a point:

> If an L (Lesbian) from the #LGBTQ community disagrees with a G, which one is HOMOPHOBIC? According to modern VICTIMhood, one must be!

> But then what if a Black man and an Asian woman disagree, who is at fault: the sexist or the racist? The guy in that equation by modern WOKEism must be sexist, and the Asian woman must clearly HATE the Black guy and is racist!

> Seriously, these are the automatic assumptions and pre-ordained conclusions that must be jumped to immediately without any real clue as to the CONTENT OF CHARACTER of any involved or examination of any FACTS. If any of said victim class is involved in any situation, there JUST HAS TO BE either racism, sexism, or PHOBIC root cause of some kind. Hold on, let's look at this week's victimology hierarchy chart. One thing is clear, if a STRAIGHT WHITE MALE is involved in anything, it is clearly HIS FAULT (just cause, well, you know) and is the top-of-the-hour lead on MSNBCiles. And look out if he's a CHRISTIAN rather than an ATHEIST!

> And OMG, what if the SWM happens to "identify" as a conservative Republican. * gasp * That's the

final nail in the coffin. He MUST BE GUILTY of something, anything until proven innocent (and even then, that "correction" will be buried at the back of the Newspaper)!

The Straight White Male FARCE.

He thought of the opinion and political agenda that crept in to the whole Charlottesville situation. People could easily seek out the entire press conference that was actually about infrastructure and the Department of Transportation, but instead they engaged in clear spin rather than factual reporting. President Trump, several times, clearly outlined that he was speaking about *good people* on both sides of the statues historical value debate. Some people value education and spurring on conversation, but political correctness people just wanted to tear down and censor discussion; they need to tear down the monuments, and those wanting to preserve historical monuments have nothing to do with neo-Nazis that the President condemned three times in his speech. Marten outlined the controversy and continued further:

Hear THE ENTIRE SPEECH for yourself (and the disingenuous press badgering and trying to twist the President Trump's words, asking the same things over and over, trying to get him to muddy his statement for their own self-aggrandizement and sound bites for their news channel (implying FALSEHOODs in the way they phrased their questions)). They ultimately showed only the "very fine people" snippet COMPLETELY OUT OF CONTEXT to purposefully and willfully cause malice and peddle their false narratives.

And Democrat politicians still to this day REPEAT WHAT THEY KNOW TO BE A LIE!

On Charlottesville they continued to twist and other things you heard Trump say they've twisted...

And, of course #SNOWFLAKES on Twitter whine about #ChristianWalker (hoodie) appropriately pointing out that EVERYONE FEELS THE PAIN OF THE #BIDENflation (especially at the #GAS pump) but APPLAUD #AOC for sixteen-thousand-dollar #TaxTheRich (farce) Dress & proclaiming to be just an avg folk who cares about the poor.

How many people could that $16k have fed? How many NY folks (peeps she reps) missed out on $50k/yr jobs because of her attacks on #Amazon and passing on a warehouse in NY — while AOC lines her pockets on backs of the poor.

Candace Owens, IMO, is the **most DANGEROUS** (**#Black or otherwise**) #Woman (if there can be such as thing with today's endless identity politics insist pointing out there are over 100 #Genders now) **on the planet** cuz she threatens (w/ #FACTS, #REALITY, #LOGIC, #REASON) the #DemocratPlantation (her terms, not mine) and the constant #FASCICRATS' #RACEBAITING.

So many now INSIST you must identify and recognize RACE in society, a direct contradiction to what Martin Luther King Jr. spoke of as he strived for a color-blind society—judging purely on the CONTENT OF CHARACTER, individualism, not collectivism, separation, or SEGREGATION.

Abolitionists, the primary founders of the #Republican Party, overturned #SLAVERY while #Democrats insisted #Blacks weren't #HUMAN. Likewise, the #GOP will overturn #Abortion while #Democrats make the same false narrative today those babies are just a clump of cells in the womb and aren't human. (When has a Human ever given Birth or carried anything but a Human? I'd like to see where Democrats can prove a female human could potentially be carrying a chimp or a dolphin?)

The Republican Party was the sole driving force in getting passed the 13th, 14th, and 15th Amendments and under EQUALITY of ALL HUMANS Abortion would eventually over-turned as everyone knows, despite their denials, a #HUMAN in the womb has Rights under the 14th Amendment. And, of course, do we need discuss RACIST Margaret Sanger who is the founder of Planned Parenthood. (If you do not know her and PP's history, TRY DUCKDUCKGO searching it.)

People continue to claim #ABORTION was established as a RIGHT under Roe v Wade. It was not. Even Ruth Bader Ginsberg admitted as much in a Chicago Law School speech that to this day can be found online (which may one day be scrubbed from the Internet by left-wing platforms). Roe was decided on the narrow focus and premise, under "PRIVACY" RIGHTS. NOT a RIGHT OF ABORTION nor the CHILD'S RIGHTS under the 14th Amendment and the Left knows that, despite their rhetoric, and fear a TRUE CONSTITUTIONAL GROUNDS RE-HEARING OF ROE. This case alone a "Privacy" case but not that "Abortion" itself also that by extension. Even the most Liberal Justice on the SCOTUS at the time, Ruth Bader Ginsburg, admitting such before University of Law Chicago School in a speech.

#FromIdaBWellsToCandaceO

Long before ROSA PARKS, who the Left holds up as a GREAT HERO, IDA WELLS stood up against #RACISM and #RACIST laws! #IdaBWells refused to leave her first-class train seat when demanded to do so by RACIST WHITE DEMOCRATS (look it up, compared to Rosa on the Bus)! But IDA does not fit the current NARRATIVES. She was a real Hero, and of course the disqualifier for the Liberal Media was that she was a staunch Republican, who put her life on the line DAILY (unlike Rosa)!

Still today, people refuse to have an honest debate on ALL these issues: race, the history of Planned Parenthood and its RACIST founder Margaret Sanger who claimed it was her goal to try and irradicate the Black race, #GAYTIVISM vs just acceptance and tolerance.

Sadly, these were not thoughts he could express around the workplace. Political correctness has a firm grip on the majority of the staff, and most others, at that place, and only certain, carefully crafted opinions weaved into the otherwise strait-laced factual reporting was allowed. Such things were only addressed quietly, behind the scenes, in the corners of the paper offices.

Left-wing viewpoints had become the predominant ones in Hollywood a few decades ago, and Marten wondered if anyone had written a book on that transition. Preserving freedom and fighting communism and fascism were the themes during, and just after the Second World War years, and still a few decades beyond, but somewhere they went from calling Senator Joseph McCarthy, who was sounding the warning of communist infiltration, as paranoid and a loon, about communists in La-La-Land, to almost all current celebrities happily making films hating on America and capitalism. Hollywood scripts that could seemingly have come direct from the staff at Pravda, or as GIJIAS would prefer, wanting to tear down the West.

The great, and a hero, and inspiration, of Marten's favorite journalist, Bernard Goldberg, was really the first to do a deep dive into the how, where, and when—but not necessarily the why—of when so-called mainstream media outlets took the leap into full-on Liberal bias, which was indeed the perfect title for Bernard's book (*BIAS – a CBS Insider Exposes How the Media Distort the News*) in Marten's mind. He wishes he could get everyone to read that book and take the red pill as made popular from *The Matrix*, though Marten prefers *The Thirteenth Floor*, based upon the book *Simulicron-3*, movie that landed up being swept aside and supplanted, losing its forerunner, and true leader, status in the generic matrix like thought films.

8

9/11

EARTHSHAKING FIRE FROM THE CENTER OF THE EARTH
WILL CAUSE TREMORS AROUND THE NEW CITY.
TWO GREAT ROCKS WILL WAR FOR A LONG TIME,
THEN ARETHUSA WILL REDDEN A NEW RIVER.

—Quatrain 1, 87, *LES PROPHETIES,*
De M. Michel Nostradamus

arten knew that 9/11 would be by far the toughest chapter to address. Covering the most effective act of war (not withstanding the Revolutionary War, War of 1812, and the US Civil War) since Pearl Harbor against the United States could never be done with enough justice. There was just no way to convey the historical significance that the attack inflicted upon the nation, its economy, and citizens from all over the world; a true attack on all peoples, including fellow Muslims.

That mass murder shocked the nation like never before. People could cope with everyday violence, even murder, but not in recent memory was that degree of inhumanity, in one coordinated effort, unleashed on this nation, which called into question the very nature of humankind to conceive of such evil.

Marten, himself, had unwittingly become numbed to some of the horrors of everyday life. Reports of the untimely demise of countless individuals had slowly hardened his view of daily life and its risks. While one hundred sixty thousand people on average die per day, the cruel nature of a small percentage of society that inflicts undue suffering on the masses through criminal acts of aggression is devastating.

In the days following the fateful event on September 2001, Marten's nightmares began. He had become jolted into a new sense of enlightenment and questioned his own humanity. How much had he been to blame for allowing the world, from what was within his control, to turn a blind eye to those in trouble. What had he failed to do to make the world a better place, and perhaps help to foster such immoral activities?

Marten had certainly always cared. It greatly saddened and troubled him that he was too acutely aware, being a journalist and all, of humanities dark side. That there could never be a developed society that would provide for and please all. There would always be those disaffected who turn to criminal activities. There would always be a sector of the populace with violent tendencies. There would always be people who aim to acquire money, prestige, and power. Some would stop at nothing to attain that power and think little of the lives they trample over in their quest.

Despite modern advances in technology, seemingly bringing some nations and citizens closer together, those same advances provided the greater opportunity to spread hate. Divisive individuals use cultural and religious divides to continue to drive a greater wedge between the peoples of the globe rather than attempt to promote peace and coexistence. The stirring of emotions—hate, fear, jealousy, and even a warped kind of love—is being employed on a daily basis to force conformity and provide power of the few over many.

While evidence of all these truths had been present, the sum total had somehow seemed to go uncalculated. Events, like dots, just were not connected. By processing bad news as unique and separate activities seemed to somehow make the sorrows manageable. The emotional impact was diminished and made more bearable. September 11 changed all that in the minds of many.

Now all things were related. The forces that lay beneath sniper attacks in the Phoenix Arizona area were no longer seen as isolated but connected to things like the seemingly random acts of violence on the streets of Detroit. The District of Columbia sniper attacks that were more widely covered, especially via TV media, about DC area sniper assaults were later solved. They were finally tracked down based upon eyewitnesses to the events and surveillance cameras pinpointing the existence of a suspicious blue Chevy Caprice. The Beltway Snipers, as they came to be known, engaged in assaults in several directions out from DC but predominantly in areas with residents related to US government. But, sadly, many still remained unsolved.

Jamaican-born John Allen Muhammad had determined he would kill and cause terrorism in the name of Allah early on his days in the United States. It wasn't until he met someone he could indoctrinate into his hatred of Western culture, and someone willing to take up arms in the name of the GIJIAS along with him that he decided to act. He felt they could evade capture if they used high-powered long rifles while hidden from the trunk of that Caprice. They planned quick hits and then quietly and carefully, abiding by the street laws, slipped away.

Lee Boyd Malvo, just seventeen years of age at the time, was later convicted despite claiming he was under undue influence of the adult Muhammad and not acting "of clear mind" and was imprisoned, captivated, controlled, by Muhammad. Their spree lasted only over the month of October 2002, but the fear of copycat attacks remain to this day.

Following 9/11, the root cause of these, and all other senseless acts, was drawing more scrutiny as officers suspected broader ties or inspiration – that would have otherwise been dismissed as local unrelated isolated crimes. No longer was just the excuse of evil acceptable. The very nature of humanity was now in question. Can such localized malice be treated as if it were not part of a larger whole? The passage of new terrorism laws also meant that those local domestic cases would have broader applications for criminal prosecution for the unforeseeable future.

Crime and punishment, or the lack thereof, and as we see in some US urban-centers and increases in crime there, promoted the lure of indecent acts. The failure of society to castigate this immoral faction within its midst further perpetuated the intolerable measures. The more horrific the criminal acts, the more hardened to the actions the general public grew, or worse, the more the masses just turned a blind eye and buried its collective head in the sand; that ostrich theme again, pretending, hoping the evil all around them would not touch their specific lives.

Somehow, to voluminous citizens in Western nations, crime would always be in the realm of others. The "it won't happen to me" mindset permeated the masses, despite knowing that criminal activities were taking place and being reported in their local papers. People ignored the dangers in the favor of a self-imposed "ignorance is bliss" attitude.

The many criminal acts that comprised the total overall act on 9/11 suddenly brought to light the severity of how each minor legal violation in the terrorist scheme, if one or two had been prosecuted, might easily have stopped the attack. If the criminal acts of those perpetrating the attacks had been prevented as individual criminal acts, the World Trade Center would still be standing today.

Had the hijackers' previous criminal activities been able to put them behind bars, they could not have been free to attempt the hijackings. Had they been stopped for immigration issues, the planned attacks may have been disrupted and prevented. Had the vulnerability of the airport security that would allow the criminal hijacking of the airliners that day been addressed adequately, the tragically allowed escalation of unlawful behaviors that day may have been thwarted, or minimized.

A few years later, while the world was lamenting in a heightened state of security as the 9/11 commemoration approached—everyone new that anniversaries were dates terrorists would focus on—another terrorist plot to blow up airplanes was thwarted. In 2006 a new date was added to the terrorist calendar: 8/10. August 10 would serve as a reminder to terrorists of one of the most ostentatious of plots being foiled. The plot was to destroy between six and twenty jetliners in mid-flight over the Atlantic Ocean between England and the United States.

It was later discovered that the planned assault was for August 16, but the date that would go down as the most ostentatious and outlandish attempt to even one-up 9/11 was exposed on August 10 by a failed trial run, just as Project Bojinka was.

In the 1990s a Philippines flight 434 enroute to Tokyo Japan was attacked using chemical compounds resulting in the death of a Japanese businessman, though the jetliner did not crash. Flight 434 was a trial run of, what was later discovered to be Project Bojinka. This plot targeted nine to twelve planes over the Pacific: Asia to America flights. Using chemical-based weapons that would be easily mixed on board and using a small electronics device as a detonator, the terrorists had hoped to down the flights simultaneously. It was foiled when the key Project Bojinka planner's apartment caught fire and chemical weapon mixtures and plans of attack were discovered.

Marten knew the analysis of the 9/11 topic was going to require asking many of the same questions that the Madrid incident brought up. The fate of the nation would hang in the balance following such an attack; that was, after all, the whole point of such an attack, to affect political change. The terrorists' goal was, and is, an effort to shape public opinion, to draw attention to the terrorists' cause.

Al Qaeda had already seemingly affected public opinion and shaped the outcome of the elections in Spain that year. Whether terrorist strikes that year effected the elections may be debatable among level-headed and open-minded individuals, the terrorists were definitely going to spin the turnout. Emboldened by this perceived success, their intent would be to play up the situation as a major triumph for their cause.

Marten gathered up his pad of legal paper and pen from his desk. He preferred writing physical notes. Marten found it hard to move away from the paper method of maintaining information from his early news days. Legal pages and manila folders made him feel more in control of the information. He preferred to be able to shuffle his notes about. He also believed the act of physically writing by hand helped commit the materials to memory, or at least recall where he would find them for quick reference. Inputting his manuscript into his laptop would be the final method for easy editing and submission to others.

While everything landed up in electronic form for its final manipulation into press form, he just didn't want to let his paper trail for follow-up purposes go. This practice was certainly coming in handy now that he decided to write his manuscript. Having the residual information regarding the terrorist events he'd written and saved from before would prove an invaluable resource in compiling chapters of his book. All that would be required would be to build continuity between the attacks and provide pre- and post-attack analysis.

Marten engaged the ball point of his pen and placed it to the paper. Just thinking of that tragic day was difficult. He now had to try and draw upon his abilities to be objective and, as cold as it seems, separate himself from the story as much as possible and present as impartial an analysis as he would be able to do.

The biggest question, and the one that keeps haunting the nation, was whether or not the specifics of the attack on that day foreseeable?

That was the most difficult to address, but the most logical place to start. Marten began to pen out some items needing inquiry:

- Why was 09/11//01 chosen for the date of attack?
- How might it have been avoided?
- Was this an act of aggression that could develop into other conflicts, or a global conflict, beyond the Afghanistan retaliation?
- Is characterizing the conflict as World War III outlandish sensationalism or a realistic portrayal of events still yet to further unfold?

Just how far any of these issues would be able to be pursued was an open issue in and of itself. Marten knew that many of these questions would just lead to opening up more uncertainties. He lamented the lack of history being taught in schools today. Sadly, history has been rebranded as social studies and was laden with opinions and conjecture as opposed to just the straight teaching of historic dates and only the facts and presenting stated motivations and intent when and where clear and in context.

Marten realized that most people had not learned that the contiguous States of the mainland in North America had actually been attacked during the Second World War. Sure, most people retained the basics of the attack on Pearl Harbor but few knew about *the Battle of Los Angeles* later generations only learned of from the movie by the same name.

In the first military action on United States' soil since the War of 1812, a Japanese submarine, fleet designation 125, attacked an oil field at Santa Barbara, California. Fort Stevens, Oregon, was also shelled. These were overt acts by an aggressor nation while under full declaration of war and by uniformed soldiers. The military style kamikaze attacks, just shy of a full sixty years later on the opposite coast, were to be undertaken by militant cowards not acting under a declaration of war against a nation at peace.

Another attempted Second World War assault from abroad was against a section of forest in Oregon, this attack was a response to the Doolittle raid on the Japanese mainland. However, the greenery was wet and the bombs that were dropped in order to create forest fires never happened. This was not their only attempt to create terror within the United States.

In 1945, the Japanese launched balloons that traveled on the jet stream to the US and dropped bombs all across the country, from the very edge of the California front to the Great Lakes of Michigan. Some even fell on Canadian soil. These were, in a basic sense, some of the first improvised explosive devices.

One such occurrence resulted in the death of six. In May of 1945 the remnants of an unexploded balloon bomb lay in the path of Bly, Oregon, residents on an outing. A young child encountered the device and before the child could be stopped from meddling with caused the device to explode resulting in the only known loss of life by these bombs.

Even the Manhattan Project, the most secretive project of the war, was endangered by these small-scale attacks on America—though a strictly enforced media blackout kept Americans in the dark about them then and prevented wide-scale panic. Subsequently, and equally important from allowing the actions be reported, the Japanese didn't hear any useful information about their attempts and eventually abandoned the effort.

A Hanford, Washington, power plant was shut down due to a balloon bomb coming in contact with a key utility pole, which caused the power to go out at the Los Alamos facilities in Nevada. The Japanese continued the assaults regardless of the low impact they thought the balloons were having. As a propaganda tool it was invaluable for the Japanese military to report that they were indeed engaging in striking at the heart of America.

Hitler's Germany had also devised plans of its own to strike America. After the war, it was discovered Germany had plans to build the "New York Bomber." The world's first inter-continental ballistic missile (ICBM) was in design stages, based upon advanced V-1 and V-2 rocket technology. Germany was poised to provide an unmanned airstrike upon New York City and the whole East Coast, from the very heart of Europe. Also, German-controlled bases within South America were going to be used to strike the United States, but the attacks never materialized. All history lost to all but the most Second World War historical buffs.

Few would ever come to learn of the Nazi spies that actually landed via Kriegsmarine units submersed off the coast of Florida and New York. More than a dozen successfully penetrated everyday life in North America. If it had not been for a few of them turning double agent, these saboteurs would have been free to strike all across the American East Coast and Midwest.

Marten recalled his prior writing on 9/11, an online article, where he mentioned Nostradamus and his sixteenth-century prediction that some were circulating as a popular accepted translation of one of his

Quatrain's as: "From the sky shall rain Fire… Hard as they may try, nothing shall save the New [York] City's people were to die that day."

At least that is one accepted translation from French. Nostradamus, as well as other prophets, clairvoyants, or psychics have foreseen religious wars many times. Three world wars have been foretold. We've had two such wars, and there is much speculation about what will trigger the next.

Nostradamus also spoke of this war; likely considered the Third World War, or at least the prelude to it—to "last twenty and seven years." Many were left to ponder if it was a coincidence that CNN and FOX news channels noted that the first, known, United States citizen to be killed in a 2003 terrorist attack in Beirut, Lebanon, twenty years to the day (October 23) when the United States was brought into that conflict. Marten was certainly most perplexed over the "twenty" and "seven" years statement of Nostradamus for several years post-9/11. However, it would imply that the Afghanistan War would only last seven years. The semantics being important.

It is unclear when the US defeated the enemy there versus when began the nation building—and continued Forward Operation Bases kept to tamp down flare-ups that could be defined as separate terrorist actions. This complicates gauging the accuracy of Nostradamus' prediction or if perhaps he was foreshadowing another assault on the "New City" many believed to apply to New York City. It was too specific and too farfetched to be a coincidence. Was an even worse attack, perhaps nuclear, to come.

Though that particular translation became disputed as part of a Nostradamus hoax that a university student perpetrated, claiming the quatrain to be written by Nostradamus years after his known passing.

Verifiable Quatrain 1, 87 is about earthshaking fire from the center of the earth that will cause tremors around the New City. He wrote that two great rocks will war for a long time, then Arethusa will redden a new river. These events are hard to verify. Hindsight is always 20/20, as the saying goes, and it is very much an un-exact science to cross-reference modern events with any Nostradamus, or other prognosticator for that matter, predictions. Could the two great rocks be referring to the North American and European (that the Middle East resides upon) continents?

Then there is the whole matter of religious prophets. Religious texts, of all faiths, are recorded by and from mankind. We are frail, sinful being, and some of these origins go back to those who lived many years before the availability of writing instruments and material. In Nostradamus' time, the sixteenth century (AD 1500s), only the rich could afford to commit their words, views, and objectives, to a somewhat permanent record.

Texts from the sixteenth century was one thing, of course. Atheists contend the many religious texts themselves also just fanciful speculation and potentially outright fictions. They allege that the life and times of both Jesus and Muhammed were somewhat fabricated and exaggerated. With Jesus they contend he did indeed live but was merely mimicking what was outlined and foretold in the Torah. They completely ignore the miracles he performed and believe there was no resurrection. Instead, they think his followers stole the body! As for Muhammed, they contend he was just an opportunist looking to create an "us too" religion, copying much of the Old Testament and New Testament and then adding on, in order to garner power and control over fellow Arabs. Much of the religious writings was handed down in an oral tradition and prone to revisions and embellishments based upon any given storyteller, they contend. Nostradamus, it could at least be noted, wrote his own text, which was then translated later.

Another puzzlement to Marten was about reconciling Nostradamus' third world war predictions with his cross reference to Christ's Bible that man would have his own free will. Marten greatly hoped that many of Nostradamus' predictions would never come to pass, or perhaps that the outcomes would be altered; some historians feel that some of the predictions were wrong. Did some change the fate of humanity? Did some come true? History is still open to interpretation and that, or other events yet to come application, possible conclusion.

Marten was not comfortable with the implication of some of the predictions. Marten considered himself a man of faith. He does not, however, reject all other religions out of hand. None of us, certainly, were around thousands of years ago. Humankind was left to preserve and pass on the word of any given faith, whether it be of his or anyone else's faith. Many of today's religions, after all, are offshoots of other religions. Disagreements over interpretations of the texts or arguments within one faith leading to new denominations or even all new religions.

Marten holds to his belief, he is firm in his beliefs of Jesus Christ as his Lord and Saviour, but he wasn't certain that the writings were all infallible. He left open the possibility that fallen mankind may have introduced some of their own interpretations, pre-conceived notions, or biases while passing on the Word. With each translation or transliteration, the words might have evolved and changed focus. In his opinion translations from the original Aramaic, Greek, or

Latin that changed just a few words here and there could have grave implications on an overall context of a passage or passages.

Marten believed the question of textual integrity should be part of the overall discussion, and that everyone should take to heart that we are all captive to the misgivings and frailties of the human condition. Part of that human condition is there are liars, con artists, cheats, and opportunists amongst us now, just as there were thousands of years ago.

Marten knew religion is one subject that sets off passions, debates, and suspicions, as much as talk of politics between rival political organizations. Most people just cannot handle anyone mentioning anything that could shatter their fragile grip on their beliefs – religious or political. Marten needed to write in a manner that would not ask anyone to question their faith but just to realize that over time many religious texts have been translated, re-translated, and re-worded for a more current context of the diction of the times. Though the ever-growing information from beyond the initial discovery of the Dead Sea Scrolls, is proving that much of the Jewish and Christian texts have remained as true as possible to that what was intended to be preserved long-term.

Marten thought everyone who is religious should pray that they be shown the way, and that we may be forgiven if wrong. Whether you praise Allah, which is the original Aramaic word for God, Christ, the Holy Trinity, Scientology, or a deity without definition that might be influenced by aliens (Greek or Mayan gods or otherwise), we need to respect each other as individuals and remember our religious texts passages on forgiveness and treating fellow mankind with a sense of coming together rather than division. Love your neighbors as yourself—even care and pray for your enemies.

Marten made a brief notation on his yellow pad, in the way of a reminder, that his book should explore the issue of how a single man (Usama bin Laden, Adolph Hitler, David Koresh of the Branch Davidians, etc.) can manipulate those weak in the very faith they claim to adhere to. Many ignorant of the details of their own faith, out of sheer laziness on their part or just not knowing how to interpret what they read, make themselves vulnerable to manipulation.

Marten considered this idea of manipulation and felt far too many people were being manipulated and that there was an increase in cults and fringe religious factions. By teaching and twisting just small passages of the 'Koran 9/111' passage, for instance, he felt served as a basis for twisting those susceptible to hate to believe the attacks on 9/11 would be justifiable and preordained.

Marten wondered who made the distinctions? Whose perspective was correct? Marten wondered if he was one of the ones on the outside looking in or on the inside looking out or right in the thick of it all. It seemed to him that we all have to be vigilant nowadays.

Marten ruffled through his papers and came across a notation from a potential news report from early March 2003. He penned a brief note on the page to perform a *Lexus-Nexis* search confirming the information. The story was about an East Coast state whose legislature had invited a Muslim cleric, as it was reported, to speak to the legislative bodies of government. One of the state's representatives boycotted the session because of the planned guest speaker. There is simply no other way to look at this as blatant prejudice, Marten thought. The cleric was not a radical or extremist, as far as anyone contending, that had twisted his faith in order to incite hatred against another group of people (non-Islamists, in this case). If the guest would have been a known terrorist sympathizer and supporter, that would have been different. It was not as if Usama was paying a visit to the state.

In Marten's mind, so-as to avoid utter hypocrisy, we cannot fight an enemy, nor call them an enemy, if we act in the same manner—except for some iterations of necessary retaliation in the 'Fight Fire with Fire' vein. Some enemies will only back down, if met strength for strength, strategy for strategy; even is sometimes distasteful such a manner may be to react. How can anyone not understand this? Some form of communications must be attempted from time to time. Are we not to have any dialogue between those we do not yet fully understand? How could there ever become any understanding between peoples without dialog? He glanced again at his double underlined entry: "I sure hope this Representative does not get reelected!" The cleric, he believed, wished to express condolences and promote understanding and peace.

This reminded Marten that he also wanted to somehow impress in people's minds the issue of hate crimes. The very notion was racist to Marten. Making a crime more horrible than another just because of the race or creed of the people involved is unconstitutional; we are constitutionally bound to not discriminate based on race or religion. That was a different subject all together, however, and Marten refocused. He knew it was important that Americans not overreact based on an individual's look. Arab Americans as a group were in no way the enemy any more the majority of Japanese or German Americans during the Second World War were the enemy. It is, of course, obvious, and stupid, to overlook the fact that there may be a greater risk from certain groups. Marten expected everyone to be on their best behavior and respect each other as individuals.

Since Marten resided in southeast Michigan, he thought that the area was more in tune with those of the Muslim faith since southeast Michigan had the highest concentration of Arab Americans than anywhere else in the US. But, of course, not all Arab-Americans are Muslim, and not all Muslims are Arab descent. As Marten made notes, he wrote the hyphenated American thing, which he disdained. He felt it just led to more discrimination and lack of assimilation. Anyone that insisted on being called a hyphenated American had suspect loyalties. Are they American or not?

Marten thought about an event that occurred in Blissfield, Michigan where an American immigrant from Iraq was charged with arson for burning down his Dairy Queen. The franchise owner claimed it was a Desert Storm veteran who targeted him because of his Iraqi background. Such hate hoaxes, for whatever reason, be it financial or political gain or just craving attention, sadly happen far more often than people think. There are many instances of people putting hateful graffiti on their buildings and then setting them on fire in a ploy to gain media attention or promote a false narrative to smear their political opponent as being racist or xenophobic. In fact, it's usually the case that the one doing the smear campaign is desperate and losing and desperate and engaging in tactics they hope will somehow miraculously turn the tide in their favor.

Marten expected that Iraqi Arab Americans would act with exemplary behavior, and that indeed had been displayed in the War on Terror as they generally cooperated with the FBI and Homeland

Security, during both Gulf Wars and subsequent uncertainty of Iraq's future.

September 2003 an Arab-American summit was held in Dearborn, Michigan, with various levels of local, state, and federal government officials, including Homeland Security, the FBI, the CIA, and the NSA. The Arab Americans were caught between the love of their adopted country, the United States, and their grave concerns for family or friends still in the Middle East. These interactions and events, and 9/11, do not operate in a vacuum. All events effect other actions and cascade regarding supplementary events.

Marten paused from compiling these fresh notes and recalled they seemed so familiar. No doubt he'd covered many of these items in an article he had written in 2003, which provided a retrospective on his thoughts of 9/11 then. Sure enough, when he checked his archived copy of the article that was now long gone from its original recesses of the Internet as the original place it was posted now defunct; only now found via the *Wayback Machine* Internet Archives services by anyone looking for it. That would be the easiest place to gain and bring in his thoughts and would then just need some updating.

Yes, that would save, in regard to the 9/11 chapter of the *Terrorist Tracks* book would be concerned, a lot of his time and efforts. Yes, he thought more and more as he examined the archived article on-line these themes as previous thoughts were indeed in there. What else would be too he contemplated.

He printed out the blog; one of many he wrote under a pseudo name to maintain a separation from himself and his professional life and he could express opinion he would always have to avoid in his professional capacity while doing his official newspaper work; to add to his stack of hand-written notes and quickly saw when he perused his article, he saw that he offered some commentary in the form of books or movies that he was recommending be read or viewed. He didn't think such a presentation would be a very viable strategy, but he read on using a yellow highlighter, marking up key pieces to incorporate into this project. He knew some things would need be changed to modernize the older text:

August 2003

Bringing several of the issues outlined here-in— terrorism, war abroad, discrimination, our past abuse of Japanese Americans during WW-II, with those of terrorism and a provocation to war (question, or statement – you decide)—it has already been done. One can best relate our current quandary by reviewing the Denzel Washington / Bruce Willis Film *"The Siege."* The film raises the issues we currently face but extrapolates conditions that could happen if we do not act now. Do we dare wait until the Bronx or S.E. Michigan turns into the war zone at the heart of the Middle east crisis? This film is not so far-fetched!

If you recall events late in the year 2002 and early 2003, one will recall the arrests and break-up of an Islamic terrorist cell in the Bronx, and some arrests in the Dearborn, MI, area. One would recall the mosque in the Bronx that was identified as an Al-Qaeda fund-raising organization. There were also public reports on a Buffalo Al-Qaeda cell that was broken up in NY. Then there are the FBI and Homeland Security Offices actions and arrests that we do not hear about. NOTE: I use the Al-Qaeda spelling of the organization (as I've seen it spelled a half dozen different ways since, but most settle on Al-Qaeda), despite how it was first portrayed by the News broadcasts and the terrorist's organizations identification.

The movie *The Siege* also grapples with America's past, specifically World War II and the treatment of Americans of Japanese descent. Could we come to the point where the United States of America would declare martial law and round up those of Arab descent? What about rounding up, discriminating against, individuals on the basis of their religion - the freedom of which is expressly protected in the Constitution of the United States? Other constitutional rights have been eroded! The moral fiber and basis of our constitutional rights, which, as some contend, were drawn from the Judeo-Christian tradition, are under attack. The government may not adopt an official religion, nor is it to attack or otherwise attempt to destroy any religion of the people of the United States. The founders of our country wanted no official religion, as solely recognized by the country, nor the restriction thereof.

Are there real-world threats—threats of chemical or nuclear attack within the boundaries of the United States—today? Yes! If you believe the reports of declassified CIA briefs that stated that "In 1990, during ethnic unrest in the southern part of the former Soviet Union, most likely the Chechnya provenance. (Get prepared to hear more from them as the years move on. Maybe you'll recall the theatre attack when insurgent units attacked a USSR army facility.) The report went on to state that the nuclear weapons were compromised—that is came under the control of the rebel insurgents. As bad as the US-Russia relations were, they still held negotiations. If those weapons reached the enemies of the free world, several of the scenarios (outlined later in this blog) could very well have occurred! And indeed, the scenario in the movie *The Sum of All Fears* may become reality.

These are indeed new times. Or are they really? Failure to examine history, and confront the human tendency to repeat past misconduct, which would result in a conflict of greater proportions than a more 'manageable' fight against those who would otherwise incite others to their 'perverted definition' of their religion, rather than the true spirit of the faith. Some contend many wars were fought in the name of Christianity in the name of God, against the very nature of peace and love espoused by a peace-loving, individual freedom's loving, faithful. Same concept, different faith! Do we dare let it evolve to the degree of destruction that past wars in the name of GOD (or insert your preference deity name here) had achieved? Is that right? Since everyone wants to be so politically correct nowadays, would it be "fair" since it is, in anyone's given mind it, their turn! Can anyone say anything other than 'of course not' and be considered sane? Human? Loving? Godly? Who's turn would it be next, then, to slaughter millions in the name of whatever their religion might be?

Nostradamus, as well as other prophets, clairvoyants, psychics, or however you care to make the reference, have foreseen those wars based on religion. The World War's, of note is that many have foretold of 3 (three) such World War's, have also been predicted. If the human race had taken note, been paying attention, been willing to act before allowing the 'Clear and Present Danger' to build to such a threat that it was almost un-opposable, these Wars could have been averted. Yes? Or are they ordained by a higher authority or just human stupidity? Is this WWIII? Will the actions we take today indeed avert a greater scale war? Will the actions of today, and the nature and/or relevance of the United Nations and/ or NATO and how it could be abused, actually bring about WWIII? Can we be certain? That is the stirring debate. Will the UN be somehow convinced that the

United States is the real threat to world peace and stability? Some, even among our own citizenry, are making such thought processes. There is generally a normal passage way to the nature on humankind's sin, and therefore a form of free will, for better or worse that no amount of considered years of being more and more civilized will avert.

Meanwhile, the suffering of those directly affected, as well as those indirectly affected (the entire country, as the entire U.S. has been impacted, shocked, altered, etc. by the terrorist attacks) continues. People still need assistance. People in the future, will need assistance, whether or not any further terrorist attacks occur within the United States.

That is why I feel compelled to state an opinion and stray from my desire to avoid a political stance within this article. In my opinion, the American Red Cross was viciously attacked over its handling of the funds raised in the name of '9/11' and helping the victims. The very notion that every dollar that would come into the American Red Cross would/should just haphazardly hand out checks to anyone passing by claiming to be a 9/11 victim.

Pain and suffering usually never ends in a day, in a week, over a year! Many will be suffering and at a great loss for many years to come. Some have lost someone (or more) they love, in cases some have lost their income, some may require (from injuries) Health assistance for the rest of their lives! So, what good does it do those persons if the Red Cross were to spend every penny in its Bank accounts to run its organization and fund future relief efforts (including those I've referenced here, in order to help someone 10 years from now due to 9/11 related suffering?). The absence of Common Sense abounded around this issue! And the political appointment and appeasement that followed is just as disgusting and disgraceful. If you don't understand that last statement, then go back and refer to the beginning about paying attention to the real world and what is happening around you, the terrorist attacks affect you, and you might be able to make a difference and help prevent what could be an obvious chain of events and a tragic end—if only someone was paying attention!

In fact, 2003 reports have brought to light the fact that the Red Cross is near broke. They are borrowing money in order to help Disaster relief needy. Your help is needed. donate blood, time, money, or whatever you can!

There have been plenty of individuals and groups that have taken advantage of the aftermath of 9/11 to profit personally by purposefully committing fraud and collecting, raising, selling items in the name of fund-raising, under false pretense. The American Red

Cross, and many other fine nonprofit organizations, are not doing so.

Remember I spoke of opportunists that have made personal financial gain in the name of the 9/11 tragedy? You have, undoubtedly noticed hyper-links (above, to the right, and below) to material that I reference in this article. Let me state, in the name of full disclosure, that links to the materials do constitute a cooperative agreement between myself and the organizations from which you are (would be) being linked. So, if you choose to use these links, I THANK YOU, as you help me fund the site that makes articles like this one online and available. If you choose to go elsewhere to locate/obtain these materials, I have no problem with that - as the intent of this article is to provide some insight and some understanding regarding the events of our Time and not to use/abuse this forum as a blatant attempt to profit from others suffering. Some of the reference material provides a look at the threats we faced, others directly relate to the current threats against us, while others provide food for thought in general, as outlined above.

Marten realized that last paragraph would most definitely have to be reworked upon placement into the final manuscript, if it were to be at all. He scribbled himself another note about it in the margins and resumed, his trip back to his 2003 mindset, reading:

The most important movies that you could view would be *The Siege* (marshal law, terrorism in NY, massive profiling, suspension of Civil Rights) *The Sum of all Fears* (it only takes one bomb, and just a couple of people), *Collateral Damage* (time to learn the reality of unrest of any kind, and those it inadvertently effects), and *Executive Decision* (terrorists with a loaded plane of innocent passengers, will the President OK the shooting down to save all of Washington DC and condemn 1,000+ passengers).

These are all related very closely to the war on terrorism and what is trying to be prevented.

Another, more recent movie needs to be added to the list of films to see. While a fictitious portrayal, *Tears of the Sun* starring Bruce Willis deeply probes into the consciousness of for whom, how long, at what cost, do we pick and choose our battles. I did not join the military, and regret that fact in retrospect. As *Captain America'* as I have told you some have come to call me, I have received my knowledge, training, tactical and survival skills, from alternative sources.

I have the utmost respect for the (Leave no man behind) Ranger's philosophy that should be the doctrine of our entire military. The other elite services of the elite first in/last out Marines, Navy Seals, Green Berets', and other outfits whose names you will not know of, officially, for many years. As well as the other ultra-secret forces of the CIA and NSA that you'll never learn of for at least 5o plus years when documents become de-classified.

I know this article is long, getting even longer, but if you 'really' want perspective, I ask that you hang in here with me, or break up reading the article in sections, as suggested at the beginning.

Remember, PLEASE give donations to several charities of your choice that will continue to help those currently in need, and those who will come of need. I hope the best for you, however in today's World, the donation you make today may serve your own need later due to man-made, or natural disaster, or even terrorist attack. I certainly hope the best for our country. For this issue to really be understood, and to make everyone take to heart that the threats are real, and no one is safe, chain reactions can/will affect you no matter where you reside.

To gain insight into the fanatical mind of a terrorist, and to help drive the previous point home, terrorism, whether foreign or domestic, the movie *Collateral Damage* (apart from the typical Arnold saves the World aspect of the movie) does provide perspective; as well as Arnold's *True Lies* movie. Just remember, we have had terrorist actions taken in the name of this or that by peoples of all Colors, religions, and/ or whatever other background you wish to associate them with/by. Therefore, the premise of Columbians in 'Collateral Damage' and fundamentalist Arab/ Islamic within 'True Lies' is not the focus of the 'people' portrayed as committing the acts, but of the acts themselves, their potential, etc. of how we can/may be exploited and taken advantage of by or because of our 'freedom' nature.

It is <u>not</u> the portrayal of the race, religion, etc.... of the terrorists in any of these fictitious creative licenses that they Authors/Directors (except for those based on real events) that matter, but that the threats are potentially real and from <u>Any group foreign or domestic no matter their skin tone or religious and/ or political affiliation.</u>

So many thoughts. So many problems. So many issues. September 11 was a tragic event in and of itself, yet so many other actions immediately come to mind. The 9/11 attacks represent a microcosm of the war on terror. Marten's mind raced with ideas that the country needed to seriously address. Can this one manuscript handle the degree of the seriousness and varying concerns? he thought, contemplating how to speak to everything within his book.

For now, Marten was content to just continue to provide his thoughts and concerns facing the nation that 9/11, and its aftermath, had touched off. The final determination, difficult decisions of what to keep and what to cut would need to be made later, but a complete list of the points should be accomplished to allow for the later determination.

Marten reached down to the desk to retrieve his bottled water for a quick refreshment. A quick glance at the digital clock on the desk, and he noticed several hours had passed, seemingly quickly, during this session to gather some direction for his manuscript. After a few sips to quench his thirst, he returned the bottle to the desk and devoted his attention to his ever increasingly cluttered legal pad. He did not realize that he had already scribbled a dozen pages of information.

Marten had not even needed to refer to his files. Apparently, his desire to publish a book on the subject had kept this information readily available in his memory. Flipping the pages within his printed version of his article, he used his highlighter to mark more points and then again drifted into the recesses of his mind for other pressing concerns he thought would require attention and as were continued in his past 9/11 writing:

There are extremists on all sides of political and religious issues. You are affected, whether intentionally, or through collateral fallout of the events. Consider some home-grown terrorists and terrorist attacks from those, in their minds, justified Americans:

Unabomber (Ted Kaczynski)

Oklahoma City (Timothy McVeigh and Terry Nichols)

Birmingham Abortion clinic (Eric Rudolph) murders in the name of GOD

Attacks on urban sprawl and/or mankind's ruin of the earth, by the Ecoterrorism (Earth Liberation Front)

The ELF group did not seem to care that the burning of homes and vehicles put more pollution into the air then that which they destroyed would over a long period of time, nor did they care about the deaths they caused in the name of their cause!

Collateral damage, the effect and not the movie, in an armed conflict, war, or even in everyday law enforcement, there are sometime innocent lives that are lost or people injured unintentionally and/or due to unintended consequences of the actions being taken for 'good'. The question you must ask yourself is, when, where, by what methods, how many lives affected from collateral damage is acceptable—as it is indeed inevitable and unavoidable! Think about that for a minute in relationship to WWII and the United States use of atomic weapons. Countless innocent Japanese citizens died. Was it justified in order to shorten the war and save US casualties? You may want to actually think about that term now!

Those members of Al-Qaeda who flew the planes into the World Trade Center considered that they were undertaking a 'Battle action' and fighting a holy war or Islamic jihad (with the later, further lending credence to the implication that they are not fighting for a country, for freedom, but to eliminate all nonbelievers of particular faiths). To them all the airplane passengers, all in the WTC towers, all surrounding the area, all others effected (financially, economically, emotionally, etc.) were all collateral damage and considered an acceptable loss as an act of war against the infidels of the United States. They were all collateral damage of the intended 'targets' of the financial 'symbol' and markets of America, as well as military command and control of the Pentagon and the White House or Congress. They, those who follow in the same vein, have no remorse for any of those innocents.

By comparison, aggression, whether preemptive, defensive, or otherwise, taken by the United States has a stated policy that innocent lives, non-combatants, be minimized. As a matter of fact, until just recently, some time under Clinton and reaffirmed under Bush 43, that Executive orders were signed, authorizing the assassination of Heads of State and/ or other key governmental agents of other nations to preemptively protect ourselves. Also, by contrast, the United States uses military hardware, uniformed troops, etc. to perform 'battle operations.' Invariably mistakes, human error, equipment malfunction, bad intelligence causing an inappropriate target, etc. will cause collateral damage.

When President Bill Clinton authorized Cruise-missile attacks against Iraq, the Iraq regime tried to portray the incident as an act of aggression against innocent Iraqi's, including children, on what they deemed an 'aspirin' factory. Was it? Was it dual use to make, or used to make, aspirin, but also used to make chemical weapons? We may never know. How can anyone disprove the negative? Marten pondered. Will raising these issues be enough to get people to start objectively viewing the purposefully slanted and directed biases governments, terrorists, and others, would wish be portrayed, to be questioned?

I will give our President a pass on this one. It was either, in my mind: a real legit target with 'human shields', bad Intel., fronted (false info / dis-information) to provoke an attack, or just plain mistake - none of which I think were done with/in malice toward the Iraqi people.

The main question to ask yourself is - Do you see a difference between the two types of combatants? No side is in the 'right' when collateral damage occurs, however - the fact that one (not just stating the U.S. versus whomever here, but in all conflicts around the globe) side abides by the internationally accepted 'rules of engagement' if/while the other does not - makes a difference, does it not?

There are, supposedly, many 'terrorist' nations; or nations that sponsor un-official and/or unconventional war tactics against any perceived enemy. Why then, do these nations not officially declare war on their enemy and fight? Why do not these nations unite as allies to fight their 'supposed' common enemy? Is it because this is more about 'individual power' and money as opposed to a true alliance and a real common enemy? We can see some of the same philosophy in political groups here in the United States, whereas the group leadership isn't so much as concerned about 'fixing' the perceived problem, but instead maintaining their power trip by letting the issue/condition continue to exist to generate loyalty to them, income to them, power to them, etc. Can, or will, you be able to honestly ask yourself these questions and be objective in your analysis? You must think through the issues, and leave your personal stance on the issue(s) at hand aside!

Now that we are near closing, let me again ask that you help your local charities as well as the national relief agencies, as there will always be people in need. Even better would be if you would actually donate some of your time and get involved and see what is really happening with your, and others, donations - it is really easy to write a check and mail it off. The hard part is having the courage, honesty, and conviction, to ask if you are 'that shallow' to think that by sending some money you have done all you could?

Marten noticed that part was certainly going to require some re-working. There would be no directing people from his book to now defunct webpages. Certainly, he could seek out the information, now removed, in the recesses of the *Wayback Machine* Archives for sharing, but such links are long and cumbersome. The only way they could be shared would be via one of the few available link-shortener sites. Marten used to use such service through Google, but for whatever reason they ended offering that convenience to Google users.

Now that we have dispensed from the neutral stance. Let me state that I hope we head back into Somalia, if we aren't secretly in there already, to hunt down Adid and drag him through the streets for all to see like they did our Blackhawk KIA and the capture of James Durant.

I've been meaning to put an update together for this article for quite some time, as I sit here on Friday August 16, 2003 (in regard to this power outage subject); the much-hyped 'Blackout of 2003.' Some reported a lightning strike on the United States side of Niagara Falls others on the Canadian side. The final report was that it was human error and system failure, a combination of goof ups, but there is a very good possibility that –the people of the northeastern and southeastern parts of the United States and Canada respectively were the targets of an overt and intentional act of terrorism. –All the options seem plausible.

As you see this is not the first time that such an occurrence has taken place over the currently affected areas on August 14, 2003. This very same occurrence had happened in 1965, and at that time took more than 12 hours to correct the problems. In 1977, after similar failures, the federal government, of the United States of America, assured the citizenry that studies would be conducted and the proper adjustments to the aligning system grids would be fixed with built-in redundancies to prevent any such future occurrences; it certainly does not give one great confidence in our government that still left 26 years later such a failure would, and indeed did, occur.

Terrorism? Certainly, we shall never really know, (as we may never know whether the jet over PA on 9/11 was shot-down, as reported by some initially then retract (and some Conspiracy-Theorist minded individuals contend evidence still leans toward) as we had such setting precedence within many people's memories.

The most disturbing thing about this is that there is now an established trend! London went dark, under the same claims of Grid failures. Italy went dark next.

The cause according to some sources is one electrical line fed all the way down from Switzerland was knocked out by a fallen tree. Does Italy not have any power plants of its own? One line from N. Europe to S. Europe and only Italy was affected! It can drive you insane pondering the coincidental nature of these events or if there was indeed a coordinated attack!

Fact often bears itself in the reflection of copycat, or similarly planned and scheduled, types of attacks. Premeditated attacks on a nations power grid are not new. In Australia, a 36-year-old Pakistani born architect was convicted of such a terrorist scheme slated for 2004. The individual had IED (Improvised Explosive Device) materials, maps of the Australian power supply grid, and an Urdu-language manual which outlined terrorist techniques, similar in nature to the Al-Qaeda's terrorist's guidelines and manual.

Marten was a bit reluctant to suggest the electrical grid outage was a terrorist plot, as when his news agency covered it; nor in his online article; and seemingly all others, gave a complete pass on the story. No conspiracy, but a definite pass on tough investigatory reporting into the concerns over prospective involvement. Any subsequent investigation now, would prove difficult.

Marten briefly took up another drink to quelch his now aching dry throat, and then back to the 2003 blog print-out:

As the war on terrorism continues, we must put our best face forward, but let us not be pessimistic and give the government the benefit of the doubt in this certain circumstance; regardless we have once again proven our own inefficiencies and susceptibilities to easily planned, locally schemed and funded with low budget, style of attack on American soil.

I am again adding additional 'food for thought', as I sit here dictating, watching the Arnold Schwarzenegger movie *'End of Days'* Which could prove to be prophetic in some sense, but not likely. Prior to this movie, I just finished watching, *'The Sum of all Fears'*. As I've stated earlier in this blog, the sum of all fears is indeed a rouge splinter terrorist cell, that need nothing more than to study history, search the Internet for the tools necessary, and carry out threats that existed and it succeeded in our recent history; as we as Americans have such short attention spans.

Some say that it is ridiculous that our current American administration has/is calling this a pre-emptive fourth World War. You need not be religious to believe in such a type of prediction or prophecy. One can certainly point to the Bible and the battle of Armageddon; it is indeed very hard to separate religion from this type of discussion; as the Third World War has been predicted by many prophets; many far from associated from any established religion.

As I had previously alluded to Nostradamus, one can just look back at his predictions of World War I, the rise of Hitler and World War II, the Napoleonic wars, and much more. The trouble there was his constant fear of his predictions becoming known widespread during the time of his life; as many involved in such predictions would certainly desire a different outcome from what the man who could see time saw what would come to pass. However, it is impossible to completely remove religion from this argument, as all the wars fought in the name of a greater deity, were generally not the result of the great public outcry of an entire religion, but more of a pariah infecting a sector of and taking their religious full faith and belief in, or an unwillingness to stop what they must have surely known would be great catastrophe and loss of many innocent lives.

In fact, Hitler's regime used Nostradamus' predictions of victories over Europe and dropped the Prophets predictions. The tables, of course, turned when the allies used the later Quatrains with the same predictability of outcome! Still a cynic?

Nevertheless, let us for the sake of argument, once again try to, and remove religion from this discussion. Let me beg your indulgence, and let us just assume the what the great Nostradamus foresaw through the Cold-war, the many new advances in the military industrial complexes ability to create and perfect such weapons of war, that Nostradamus describing in his modern terminology.

Many quatrains, spoke of pigs and their flying machines in order to wage war against enemies over long distances. What, pre' tell could those pigs have been that he was describing as best he could with the limits of the language of their time; not to mention the fact that Nostradamus wrote in many cryptic and changing written styles, to preserve his predictions yet protect himself against those who would do him harm in his time of the early sixteenth century. That's right and is deserving of repeating, the Nostradamus predicted the rise, second of all World war, near some 400 years before the events were to occur.

It is with all that setup that wishes to endeavor into current events. Paraphrasing Nostradamus, and of course the years and years of interpretation, reinterpretation, and potential forging and rewriting of his great works. Just like, I have mentioned about our religious texts! He often spoke about the new world, and in speaking of the 'New World' (as the America's continents were not yet discovered at the time of his writings), it often went further to mean 'the New city' or 'New York'. Later in separate Quatrains, predicted from the sky would rain fire on to the new city, though they would try, nothing could be done to save the lives of those who were to die that day.

'Day would become night, as the great city fell.' In retrospect, as is always the case with hindsight being 20/20, what did he see, he had not known of airplanes, yet describe the pig faced like creatures, that would navigate such machines of destruction from the air. Look at today's modern fighter jet fliers, there need for speed and high altitudes and maneuvers that would otherwise be beyond human capabilities, if it weren't for the sophisticated oxygen and communications mechanisms built into today's modern pilot headgear, and therefore look like beings with pig's snouts.

If you had never seen such the likes all of man's darker sides of inventions to come over the next four and five hundred years; you too would be hard pressed to find words to describe what you were seeing; but in retrospect, it is again, fairly apparent to make the match. The darkness, and day becoming night, often predicted as a nuclear strike, on New York city; remember my mentioning the term 'Ground Zero' being used. We, ourselves, of our time, have likened it to such a disaster by calling the site that has long been established as military terminology for the point of attack of a nuclear, or other large yield, weapon!

What has always puzzled me about Nostradamus' third World War predictions, and yet his cross reference to Christ's Bible that man would have his own free will, and he had greatly hoped that many of his quatrains and predictions would never come to pass, and in fact some historians feel that some quatrains are/were wrong - did some change fate?

He would have liked nothing more to be seen as a heretic, prankster, fraud, or just plain storyteller. But alas, his predictions have for the most part come true; historians had always associated in the attack on New York city as being one of a nuclear strike; which still could come to pass! Like I've implied twice thus far, ironic that we called where the World Trade Center once stood as ground zero, which has always been held in high regard as the term for the point of which in nuclear reaction of the explosion would take place, to repeat and/or re-phrase to make the point yet again. Let us hope those quatrains referred to 9/11 and not a, still future, nuclear destruction of the entire NY area.

The rain of fire from the sky, often predicted as missiles, were indeed missiles - planes turned into such weapons of destruction by those with a keen mind, and the strong determination, to strike out at the heart of their perceived enemy. Yet we cannot remove religion from this, as stated before, this comes down to a fight and fate of the whole of the world (whether this does indeed turn out to be a fateful World War III, or the attempted advancement to bypass World War III, which again not unlikely is attributed to the Middle-east by Nostradamus).

Some things in close proximity to his time, were likely easily predictable. What makes Nostradamus a sensation is that his quatrains clearly span time-frames long past his life-expectancy.

Can we indeed strike out at the head of the serpent that would cause such devastation and destruction on, as the world had never seen before -- those, my friend, are the words of Nostradamus, not mine. There was also a notion of the third Anti-Christ (again, Nostradamus' words) as one with the Blue Turban. Literal? Metaphorical? Will the enemy take heed of the warnings and lose the Blue Turban, whatever that reference does mean?

The fact alone, that it is referenced as a 'Turban,' must have some meaning and relation. What of the 'serpent' reference, any relation to a political Party symbol? Nations Flag? A long-standing (Royal, or other) bloodline's Crest? Does the Blue reference the longstanding traditional designation of the United Nations, Islamic nation's soldiers under UN command do wear light blue Turban headdress atop their helmets!

Are we to take the fact that all things are predestined, and we must just patiently wait while the world moves ever closer to its complete and almost utter annihilation? In many ways, the world is at war - it is certainly a different war than we have known before, thus far. Question is: can it stay 'somewhat contained' or will Middle-east nations in fact enter into the war. What of Iran and Syria? If they launch their army across the borders into Iraq, rather than just letting terrorists in and through (whether knowingly, or unknowingly)? Would other - rather when (basically) Islamic nations join the fight, on whose behalf/side will then join? NATO, would most likely fall apart, as it already is showing signs of doing over the entry of such countries as Turkey and former Soviet Republic nations, and the greater the alliance becomes it is inevitable the alliance built upon guarding west Europe from east/USSR/Russia/China - will buckle under the weight of a conflict the concentrates north versus south, in basic terms. religions of one sector, against religions of another sector of the, or within the alliance itself (as a majority, or whole, as most nations do not have an Official religion - some do).

This certainly cannot be a complete indictment on the Islamic faith, or even Arabic peoples of nature. It is but this subsection that we must carefully and meticulously weed out, in the name of all people and all faiths; so that we can for once truly live in peace as one group of peoples of the earth, yet indeed different in some ways, yet alike in so many others. Are we going to continue to let lunacy of the few individuals that have corrupted a group of followers to drag us down and ultimately pull us into Armageddon? It is that simple!

As President Bush succinctly put it, 'you are either with us, or against us! (In a fight against terror and/ or the abolishment of free non-Islamic designated in nature people and nations)' and to stand against us is to stand beside the terrorists and their desire to drag the entire planet into war amongst ourselves as well as them, as they seek to divide and conquer. They seek to divide us by our religions! They seek to divide us within/among our nations. They even seek to divide suspicions amongst our very own neighbors. Nevertheless, remember, they ultimately seek to destroy all nations and Peoples who are not Muslim/ Islamic in nature or support. How can anyone not understand this basic premise by now?

This is not an American war; it is a war for all nations, all races, and all creeds. The enemy is no longer a single state or two, such as war over definitive lines of France, Germany, Japan, Italy, Spain, and in the United States. The once infamous line states: 'I have seen the enemy, and he is me' let us not make that fatal mistake.

We must work together as nations, for once as the UN charter actually is meant to do, to protect not one but indeed all nations territorial boundaries and allow us to root out these terrorists whether they be amongst us within the United States, the training grounds of the Philippines, several of the Middle-eastern countries sympathetic - or just plain scared and/or bought off by the terrorists.

What of the Chechnya Republic? What of the Baltic States? What of Ukraine and Moldova? Shall they remain free and neutral in the desire to live in peace forever with each, all, and every neighbor, whether indeed sharing a border or just electronic and Internet impulse away even though half way across the globe. It is almost as if we will need to carve up the earth into separate pieces by faith, by political view, and whatever else, and move and lump all those types of people together to sink or swim collectively on their own if they cannot hold up under the weight of their own beliefs/views.

Where will China come down when it comes to the interest of north Korea (N.K.) having nuclear weapons at its southern border? Will it (China) be so foolishly short sited to see that in today's political landscape, the enemy of my enemy today is no longer necessarily allied or friendly to your nation; (That the enemy of my enemy is my friend thought process led us to arm both sides in the Iran/Iraq War to ensure a stalemate) in other than (current) appearances sake. That is, in part, what got us to where we are today with the state of Iran and Iraq. N. Korean missiles will very easily be able to be targeted at Chinese airspace, Army, Cities, and the like. Soon they (N.K.) will be able to extort their desires not just from or against the United States of America, but against all the nations of Asia. Again, I ask - can we take such chances and today's modern era and of nuclear weapons and their vast simplicity of construction, delivery, and devastation. Could China be so stupid to think that they won't be extorted for some form of monetary aide in a thinly veiled 'guise of a threat to build and/or use such weapons against China, Japan, everyone else - as they had just 4 to 6 short years ago from the U.S. when we provided $$$$ (YOUR/MY MONEY, TAX DOLLARS FROM YOUR PAYCHECK) to N. Korea on the promise they wouldn't start their (N.K.) reactor and make weapons grade materials for nuclear missiles. Once Clinton moved out of the White House, they tried to come back for second helpings, and would continue with every new Administration/President from here to eternity.

If it were up to me, I would tell the Chinese to use N. Korea as their next site for a weapons test. Actually, I'd leverage China's fear of Japan going nuclear (promising that we'd make them [Japan] a nuclear nation loading them up with plenty of Nukes in the name of Defense of Japan against a N.K. or any other nations nuclear threat) if N. Korea does not back down.

Then China can decide to deal with the problem that is truly within their 'Sphere of Influence', if you don't know or remember that phrase - then you haven't paid attention to anything about Korea, Vietnam, the Cuban missile Crisis --- Is any of this ringing a bell?? This time we play the Soviets role, with Nukes toward Japan, to get the reaction from China. HAVE WE LEARNED FROM HISTORY? If you do/have, you can prevent it from happening again, or use it to your advantage.

September 11 was not the end; it was merely just a small beginning of a greater possibility, and we have been warned. If what has been foretold, or even by happenstance has the slightest possibility of escalating to too much higher stakes than we've thus far discussed, than 9/11 wasn't Pearl Harbor (I think it's a bad analogy from the beginning - if they'd have hit and destroyed more of the Pentagon and hit the White House, then I'd agree with the concept).

Here is where the politics of the past Century gets ugly. This may invite hate mail from all over, but here goes. We are talking about history, how it turned out, what did we learn. There are plenty of 'What if's' that could have changed the course of history. As for the future, the new Pearl Harbor is yet to come, my friends. These were just the advance scouts; these were just a few mortar rounds if you will.

Now the HARD LOOK AT HISTORY and what we have been taught, what we have learned on our own, what Secret Documents recently released about the past, and what we can just plain speculate; but Nostradamus told us what was going to happen. Hitler, during WWII, used preferential Quatrains to drop leaflets over Europe where the Quatrains provided the assurance Germany would roll/rule over that next target! Please, do question all of your notions of what you have been educated to believe, just remember - to the victor go the spoils. Some History/Truth is sometimes kept (let's say, sanitized and made PC so you can feel good about yourself and your country - whatever country you might be in/ from) from the mainstream, as the Victor dictates the terms of the written history of the battles one.

Now, having said that, and further stating that I am not advocating any of the following speculations/ possibilities to have ended up different. I just want you to think for yourself. Have the information. Hold it in context. Learn from this how Governments (we're not talking conspiracy theories here, it just takes the 'Head of State' of any of these nations) to have made one change in strategy, that could've made a completely different world. We today, are at the forefront of these situations and questions that had arisen during WWII that would make the World different today - again - not arguing for better or worse, just examples of how one decision sets in motion a chain of events, and in these cases lead to the way WWII was fought and turned out.

The battle over Poland was a rouse between Hitler and Russia to split the spoils of Poland - again under a thinly veiled 'guise that Poland had advanced into German Annexed/held Territory and claimed Poland fired the first shots that started the battle for Poland. How, or why, did that have anything to do with Russia entering Poland then? Just that it was the compromise Hitler had to make with Russia, an appeasement until the time would be right when Germany and Japan were supposed to have opened a two front War against Russia. People were not paying attention! Hitler himself warned of the growing communist threat in Russia -- telling and true but ignored because we had already painted an enemy. Germany made the mistake of invading first. If they had waited until the Russians became too impatient in their desire for territorial conquest, then Hitler and Germany would have been seen in a completely different light. They would have been the protector of Poland and Smaller Annexed nations to build a Country that could bring stabilization that seven World powers (U.S., Russia, Japan, China, France, Spain [civil war fought with the assistance of Germany], and of course Germany. For whatever reason, began an arms race, vied for position and tactical superiority over who was to be their 'CHOSEN' (yes, chosen) and an inevitable conflict). That covers the War for Europe.

Moreover, what of the truth of Japan? Did they attack us 'unprovoked' as children are indoctrinated to believe, because we largely leave out the fact that we cut off their OIL - forever altering the Two Front Russian War that was to take place to crush Russia (that for the record, had the LARGEST Air Force of the day, and troop strengths that rivaled Germany's) – hindsight clearly shows Russia took the wait it out and then play our hand to conquer territory - and what of Patton's desire to march onward to/through Russia ensuring a Free World?. Could not more Atomic weapons been produced over time enough to bring an end/surrender of Moscow? Hitler was Militarily too Anxious and Stupid, and thus set the tone/motion of how WWII was to play out. Had he gone toward Russia first, what would have been made of that?

As for Japan – again, after the U.S. willfully deprives the Japanese of oil for a War they were fighting in Asia and Pacific Islands, and to have had supposed to enjoin with Germany in the defeat and divided up all of Asia. Does who fire the first shot actually define who 'caused' the War? Did the President of the United States of America knowingly and willfully expecting that we would have to inevitably have to join in on, cut the oil to Japan forcing them to stall China advancement and never opening the north-east coast of Asia and into Russia to oil reserves and production ability would have made them independent on the U.S. for anything. Did/was that move in itself a pre-emptive move to provoke Japan to in some way pull us into the War earlier – knowing U.S. sentiment was that the war that became (WWII) was Europe and Asia's problem and would could just stay out and ensure we built a defensive set of armed forces that no one would dare attack us? peace through strength, as President Reagan put it - which worked against the Socialist during the Cold-war. Yet the size of our military did not stop Japan from making the choice it felt backed into a corner to make.

Japan had two choices with limited Natural resources – to pull back and try to stalemate the War in China and move up into Russia ahead of time to get at badly needed oil reserves and production facilities, or to attempt to negotiate with the U.S. to restore its shipments of oil (sound like the Korean bribe/ extortion – see, it all fits, history repeats). Without the assurance of being able to take Russia's southern boundaries (with or without German assistance) to obtain the oil would have been a gamble. Germany had the Middle eastern oil fields to supply itself. So instead they (Japan) chose to hit us hard, as they did at Pearl Harbor where everything was so

conveniently lined up for them; and fore-stalling the
U.S.'s diversion of military power to the U.K., French
resistance, military resources to China [we sure
get lots of thanks from China and Russia for this/
that assistance.] hence, allowing Japan more time to
capture fields for self-sufficiency on the gamble they
could do it in a time-frame quicker than our repair
and rebuilding capabilities to gear up to fully take
on Japan and officially enter with great force against
Germany on the U.K. and French fronts. Let's not
forget Italy as the Third member of the 'Axis Powers'
but proved useless and a drain on German military
resources to clean up the messes it (Italy) made!?!?!
What if Italy had played a stronger role in WWII?

Again, pointing out how one thing leads to another
and having taken the other direction of any given
fork in the road may have altered what came to pass
and whether we can ever fully know the potential
consequences of our choices, these are facts, not just
conjecture, and can be traced through unclassified
Government Documents and the older History books
that worried about teaching truth, not the sanitized
politically correct indoctrination of today that always
seems to, in some way, blame America for all the
troubles of the World. Seek out the information;
it is there to be found. Do not take my word for it.
Moreover, again, these were not widespread
conspiracies, just the fate of the World in the hands

of half-dozen Heads of State. After Germany was defeated, we just conveniently forgot about the threat Russia was to pose, and in that wake allowed Russia to soak up Territories under the thumb of their large forces to IMPOSE the U.S.S.R... Again, great appreciation we got for turning a blind eye to all that from them, 'ey?

Did you listen? Are you listening? Do you care? (YOU OBVIOUSLY DO IF YOU'VE READ THIS FAR, SO I THANK YOU) or are you just content to live and let all the loved ones around you perish because you could not take the time to be bothered to think about it???? Let alone DO ANYTHING TO HELP!

Nostradamus has left us a dire warning, the four horsemen of the apocalypse are indeed on the way if this is World War 3, but we can stop it. Or Is plague, pestilence, starvation, (The first 3, of which, can be attributed to terrorist attacks or Gas/chemical warfare) deadly stockpiles of weapons of mass destruction finally be let out of Pandora's box and unleashed on the world in the lives of hundreds of millions of people: Men, Women, and YOUR children be violently, willfully targeted, and destroyed!!!

His most peculiar quatrain has to do with the final war, 'the war shall last', paraphrasing again, 20 and 7 years. This has perplexed many as the year of Nostradamus, I have since pondered if the 20 and 7 actually be the year 2007? This (one of my potential theories) opposed to set different time periods one of 20 years and one of 7 years. Perhaps it is indeed linear, and the clock started ticking on the first (relatively calm, contained fighting) just part of the early 20 years of fighting. If so, how do we define when did that time frame start? Was he using the Stars alignment, often to justify the passage of time, and therefore been using a different calendar in the sixteenth Century, could not have been, or the quatrains would not have aligned with World events? To again make people really read to digest the meanings. Just how close are we to getting to the 7 years of HELL on earth with 'Devastation, the likes the World has never seen', again Nostradamus' words, not mine. Will the Four Horsemen be released for a very HOT and Wide-open War, including low yield tactical nuclear weapons if not full-scale ICBM's. We must figure this out. We must stop this from happening!

There was the 6-day War when Syria, Jordan, and Egypt attacked Israel. WWII lasted (again, depending on when the clock started ticking - by who's terms make that distinction basically from 1939-1945. That was a long war. Let us hope that we would be willing to fight a longer protracted War as opposed to a quick 'DEFCON-1' (Defense Condition One, highest state of war, Nuclear War), turning of the Red keys, and have to start life anew in the now barren parts of the

Globe that might escape the destruction. By the way, the World will not end here and now -- Nostradamus tells us that the Earth will survive with life until the early 3700's. However, what would life be like? Will the latter of this Century turn back to living as we had in the 19th Century? Will we be living the life of the Afghans before we tried to help?

As I stated many times, we cannot leave religion out this: There is a time for every season - a time for peace, a time for love, a time for Hate, a time for war!

PS: Watch *Black Hawk Down* again, or borrow, rent, whatever and sit if once. We are about to help Liberia, (as of 08/23/03). The troops are positioning for landing to keep peace. Two words: MISSION CREEP. Be prepared for a potential HOT Zone in Liberia) and for good humanitarian reasons. This, however, is what our 'GOOD INTENTIONS' were (to help starving and oppressed peoples) in Somalia - under the stupidity of the U.N. I would love to see us send in a surgical team, grab Adid, string him up somewhere, and hang a sign around him stating 'NEVER FORGET' on the bastard! Had we maintained our military doctrine of use of preparing for any/every scenario and having, in Theatre, overwhelming and superior force, Somalia might be a Democratic Republic today! Instead, we allowed ourselves to have to depend on other nations forces for 'HARDENED' vehicles (Heavily Armored Personnel carriers and Tanks, jeeps and Hummers were not appropriate protection for that Theatre) and allowed the death of our soldiers and Durant to be a P.O.W.

Another recent film is *Tears of the Sun,* already only briefly mentioned, with Bruce Willis. It is yet another example of how our lack of involvement allows the slaughter of Millions in the name of religion. This story/movie, while not based in fact - demonstrates many incidents (Bosnia, Somalia, finishing out WWII, and more) where it is indeed representative of our lacking the courage to 'DO THE RIGHT THING'.

How long will we allow the African Continent to destroy itself over petty jealousy and ethnic and/or religious rivalries, that in the scheme of things mean that the continued fighting just continues to reduce/ deprive ALL of the very things (Food, control of Land, control of Natural resources, Blatant arrogance of power, etc.) Shall we finally take to the U.N. and tell it to Stand up and help rectify the wrongs of the World, or dissolve as another 'well intended' but miserable failure as the 'League of Nations'.

A bit of an aside, but I'll drop the name of *The Thirteenth Floor* movie in the THINGS ARE NOT ALWAYS AS THEY SEEM lesson department.

"The only thing necessary for triumph of evil is for good men to do nothing." -- Edmund Burke!

Where do you stand, do you watch someone being beaten and just pass on by, or do you do what would be the right thing to do!?!? The Sleeping Giant of the U.S. has been awakened, does our short attention span once again allow us to just return to petty PARTISAN bickering rather than see through the course that so many have foretold would happen, if we do indeed allow our Good to be absent where we could make a difference!?!?!

I am sorry to make such a transition from what I had just said above, to this statement next, but it just seems to be my time to once again step back Look, Listen, Learn, and then report back again as we move on...

May God grace us with his Mercy. No Matter What Your faith! We must settle our grievances, our differences, in peace -- The very fate of future generations depends on it. Will you, your spouse, your offspring, or your Parents be spared this horror.

Yes, it would take doing, and re-doing, to transcribe the article and edit at least some of the first-person commentary into reporting of things that have come to light from when he had written those words in 2003, but it would indeed save a ton of time rather than starting from scratch.

Some additional verbiage would, no doubt, be required. Some supplementary structure added. Great delicacy taken to address the 9/11 'Truthers' perspectives and others' views. Not addressing both sides, alternate perspectives, would detract from the objectivity. It would be up to him to report and his readers to then decide where they come down – if not them having an already hardened position. After all these years it would be hard for most to have not developed a stance in their minds. The concern then was where really to place it in the book that was not necessarily going to be chronological; as the remaining 9/11 controversies if placed to forward in the manuscript might cause some to be upset and "tune-out," potentially then opting to turn to a more 'lighter' fare type read.

9

COMIC RELIEF

THE DISTANCE BETWEEN A LAUGH AND A GOOD CRY,
IS NOT A GREAT EXPANSE.

—Anonymous

*M*arten wondered just how much comic relief would be the right balance to contain within his book as people needed some humor in their lives regardless of how serious all the things going on around them were. Would any humor be appropriate at all? What else might be right or wrong for inclusion?

Terse language proved to be a useful tool in weeding out some of the intolerant. Cursing tended to bring out the intolerance of the supposed religious types who claim to be most loving and by extension claim to be tolerant; Judging biblically as we are called to do but not condemning – when properly applying Matthew 7 "judge not lest ye be judged" does not end there but goes on to read: "for with what judgement you judge, you will be judged," as well as the other dozen or more "Judge" scriptures that adding additional clarification and context. We are called to judge biblically, and with compassion, and by same standards; not be a hypocrite – and to Vote biblically.

Mind you, using Christ's name in vain is far different than just using some four-letter words that over time had become defined as profane but are far from an affront to God that Christian biblical tenets refer. Many who have no problem with four-letter words that cause no physical harm often approve of truly hate-filled commentaries meant to wound. It's strange how those who tolerate loose verbal jabs tend to be the ones who hold in disdain those who's thoughts and actions betray bigotry and hate. In contrast the supposed enlightened thinking of a clean talking, deemed as "higher class," individuals who wouldn't think of using a "foul" word, based on their narrow-minded definitions, are the ones who allow themselves to be immediately defensive and incapable of conducting an argument because they become so hung up and flustered over so-called objectionable terms.

Marten certainly used foul language from time to time, albeit rarely and usually when stubbing his toe. The verbal ranting and curse words seemed to help distract from the pain signals. Maybe it didn't really help, but it certainly didn't hurt anything. He tried to avoid what he discerned as a complete breakdown in the English language and turn to course words merely to shock. Certainly, he knew a few kids back in his school days whose every other word was a curse. They clearly sought attention, but it had the opposite effect. They often were the most isolated and missed out on many potential friendships.

Course utterances, in Marten's mind, at times, were just another way to *emphasize* certain things. He wondered what the prudes shouted out when stubbing their toe in the privacy of their own home.

The language of many modern musical groups, and individuals, is a source of division between the youthful audience and their elders who tried to maintain what they viewed as a sense of decency. Sex sells, as the saying goes, but so too can foul language when it comes to both comedy and music. The "Explicit Lyrics" label on many musical releases attract a rebellious youth.

Today, foul language, in Marten's mind, is just a minor concern among the many troubles of modern-day society, a very low priority on the list of things to be upset about. Yet so many people still get so enraged over loose language that does no real physical harm and turn a blind eye to much more egregious offenses so prevalent in modern day life. Marten knew as long as people would allow themselves to get bent out of shape over slang terms and crude talk, there would always be another group of people willing to use that fact as a tool of dissention, pitting youth against elders and classes against each other – a complete warped sense of priorities of minor annoyances versus things that actually matter to peoples' lives and livelihoods.

More important, Marten had come to incorporate into his life another widely accepted psychological phenomena: the use of humor as a tool to regulate pain and manage depression, perceived or real negative events in one's life, and the like. "Funny," rather than "foul." Science had indeed proven true the adage that laughter is one of the best medicines. Feeling good, being happy is closely coupled with the brain's chemical composition. Happiness is a self-perpetuating notion. Laughter releases certain chemical reactions that allow us to feel good. Induced laughter through joking releases these chemicals.

American comedian physician Hunter "Patch" Adams discovered that laughter helped the sick heal faster. Whether it be solely the chemical releases or temporarily distracting oneself from the illness or both was hardly relevant, it just was clear that laughter worked. A scientific study could never really fully quantify the theorem, but it is now widely accepted as true. It is not a case of Schrödinger Cat (the hypothetical cat that may be considered both alive and dead at the same time as a result of its fate being linked to a random subatomic event that may or may not occur). You cannot treat the same patient just with medicine and just with humor at the same time. You cannot clone a patient, at least not yet, to conduct such a true legitimate comparison on the same subject under both conditions.

Laughter, conversely, could just as easily hide uncontrollable suffering from others. Thus was the case of a friend from Marten's high school years. While attending Cass Tech in Detroit, a fellow classmate and friend had hung himself in his home. He had been the class clown, and everyone had missed the intolerable pain and misery he had been experiencing.

It was from this life lesson that Marten learned that it was equally important to be able to cry. While laughter performs its function in the healing of pains of the human condition, the ability to relieve some stresses can only be overcome through tears. The tear ducts allow for the release of far more than just salty water droplets.

The comedian Robin Williams once said: "I think the saddest people always try their hardest to make people happy. Because they know what it feels like to feel absolutely worthless, and they don't want anyone else to feel like that." They use humor to make others feel good and at the same time help the depressed clown feel a bit better too, if only for a moment.

Statistics show that almost once an hour every day a veteran commits suicide. Far more than veterans, of course, suffer suicidal thoughts though. Depression and suicide know no politics, and it may be far closer to home than anyone may want to believe for one's own personal positive mental state.

Marten wrote on that too. He remembered in December 2018 a local Detroit meteorologist took her own life following a battle with pain and depression of complications after Lasik-eye surgery. He jumped back to the Internet browser and printed out his article on that. Some aspects of that article might benefit the survivors of terrorist attacks who were feeling the pain, anguish, and guilt from having lived.

He gathered the printout from the printer and again with yellow highlighter in hand set to begin another mark-up session. He began analyzing the piece:

Depression and Suicide KNOW NO POLITICS and it may be far Closer to Home than you Think/Know

(Originally published June 2018, updated Dec 2018 following the suicide of local celeb, Fox 2 News Detroit Meteorologist Jessica Starr. Transferred to *Before It's News* in 2019).

Wow! Two high profile suicides (Kate Spade and Anthony Bourdain) in just a couple days' time, but 22 veterans commit suicide daily (google: *"Project 22"*). My thoughts and prayers go out to their families.

Obviously, each person dealing with anxiety and/ or depression and those with suicidal thoughts will obviously be different, especially our veterans who are suffering from PTSD. What may seem minor events to you are major catastrophes in their mind and may lead to such a dark place that suicide is the only option. IT IS NOT!

Someone I know told of a failed suicide attempt: "It was almost surreal, like I wasn't even in control of myself as I took one pill (the regular nightly dose) and then, just took another, then several, then a handful. I have no idea how much time passed before I awoke in the hospital. And, still, 12 years on, I struggle daily with those thoughts." He tries to now use his pain for good, to share with others, let them know they are not alone and that they should reach out for help.

This is something that can afflict male or female, young or old, rich or poor. I hope that Spade and Bourdain rest in peace and their families can find peace in some way going forward. Hope you will join me in sending them your thoughts and prayers, and, if you don't mind, please include my friend that they all can find God's comfort and strength. I'd appreciate it.

Now would be a good time to reach out to all your family and friends and remind them how much you love them and how much you appreciate them being around! You are not likely to know that someone in your circle is feeling this way. Again, let me share a quote from my friend: "I can't speak statistically but only from my own circumstances/ feelings. Those who are depressed are likely to also feel that they cannot reach out to you as though you will not understand or may be dismissive or think less of them. They MAY reach out to a stranger/ professional, which is why it is important for Suicide Prevention Hotline to advertise on TV and radio."

It is important to note and understand that even the most outgoing person may have these thoughts. Some are very good at hiding it most of the time. Look at how many comedians have committed suicide.

Marten paused, thought for a moment, and then grabbed his pen. He scribbled in the margin: add Robin Williams to that list since the original writing of this article, and the self-destructive lifestyle, as evidenced by so many other comedians that passed at a young age, of the others who attempt to shorten their lives without actually going through with direct suicide. He picked the highlighter back up and read on:

Often people use humor to either deflect from their pain or in a desperate attempt to make themselves feel happy by making others laugh, at least to stave off some of the dark thoughts for some time. Again, this was something my friend has conveyed: "I know first-hand as I use humor as a coping mechanism and the times, I can make others laugh I can be Happy in that moment."

My friend also confided: "I do not know if sharing this will do any good, but something deep inside me felt it important to do so in the hopes that it could/ may potentially help even one person! I was, still am, ashamed and therefore uncertain about talking to people about it, but I feel it important. If there is even the chance I can help even one other person, then it is the right thing to do." Which is then why I share this with you!

National Suicide Prevention Lifeline

Call 1-800-273-8255

What you must recognize or need to impart on someone else that may be feeling suicidal – EVERY LIFE HAS VALUE. If it is YOU having suicidal thoughts, or you know someone having them, share all this with them. Don't let them DISMISS YOU, as they are likely to do, with the EXCUSE that you can't know what it is like and what they are going through. Don't let them believe the LIES and DARK THOUGHTS that nobody cares and nobody loves them. It is not true.

I know that my Friend and so many others still fight those LIES, DARK THOUGHTS, DEMONS daily;

they have to. They may not see or recognize the VALUE AND IMPORTANCE THEIR LIFE HAS, but it does have value and importance. Just because your mind is trying to convince you it isn't true does NOT make it the case!! Just cuz you don't see it daily or hear it from folks daily, you ARE appreciated and may be making a very positive impact on other people's lives that you just don't recognize.

Let us use by way of example the movie almost everyone has seen: *It's A Wonderful Life*. In the dramatic portrayal the main character is shown how life would have been if he hadn't lived. He was brought to recall how had it not been for his intervention a pharmacist would have caused the death of a patient by administering a wrong drug. That, clearly, is a dramatic impact. That, of course, was a movie! In REAL LIFE the influence and impact that people have on others' lives may be infinitely more subtle! It may even be INDIRECT! The influence and impact that one person has on another may then influence and/or impact another that may then have a major impact on a human life as a whole! You can be someone's Clarence (a real life, in-the-flesh angel) to help them recover and heal!

I hesitate to use another movie reference, but the *Butterfly Effect* – an actual phenom –used very drastic dramatic effects to make the Butterfly Effect point.

(The theory is that a small change can make a huge difference like a butterfly flapping its wings can set off a chain reaction of events that cause a tsunami on the other side of the world.) Maybe your influence is far more SUBTLE in REAL LIFE, the result can still have a profound effect over time or when expounded upon by additional influences/impacts projected outward!

It's like viral marketing: one person tells a few friends who tell a few friends, until half the country is talking about it. If you save a life. They save a life, then they save another. Pretty soon there are a whole lotta lives preserved. And, sorry to take this diversion, but it's like the Abortion debate. The Life saved may go on to do great and important things in life. What if down that train someone saved becomes the scientist that cures cancer? Then, legitimately, you played a part in saving all those lives too.

Again, every life has meaning and value, and the influence and impact each person has may not be easily recognized or easily measured. They are important and have cumulative effects – DRAMATIC NONE-THE-LESS AND FACTUAL! Do NOT let the negative thoughts ROB YOU OF THAT UNDERSTANDING and the positive impacts you cumulatively have on society! I don't wish to over-dramatize, but at the same time DO NOT UNDERPLAY the impact that small thoughts shared with others may play. That is simple words shared with another and then another may lead to a dramatic impact for someone else, that might SAVE PEOPLES LIVES (without going into any speculative conjecture on what they may do/accomplish in Life – that you indirectly played an important role/part in – that would NOT occur without you/them)!

It does not matter if the PAIN is physical, emotional, or both, you must try to be as understanding as possible and offer whatever help you can even if it is to ADMIT you may not heal them, but that you will be a sympathetic ear anytime they wish to have a chat and more importantly that you'll be willing to try and help them find others to aid in the healing they need.

It is one thing to lose someone at a young age to a slowly consuming disease. We can fight that, though we may ultimately lose that battle, but at least we may buy some time (even if brief moments) to help deal with that inevitableness. However, the sudden loss of someone without warning is something you likely are NEVER be able to process and get over. Constantly having to LIVE with the questions: Why didn't we notice? Is there anything we could have or should have done? YOU are NOT doing those around you a favor – just like those demons in your Head may be trying to convince you!

[OCT 2019 UPDATE: VERY IMPORTANT AUDIO/ PODCASTS YOU CAN SHARE:

WAAM Radio (AM 1600 Ann Arbor MI) THE DRIFT Radio Show - #SUICIDE PREVENTION SHOW (060918, AUDIO) - https://tinyurl.com/WAAM-Drift-SuicideIssues as well as another WAAM Show: https://tinyurl.com/WAAM-MOC-Suicide

WAAM Radio (AM 1600 Ann Arbor MI) - #MomentOfClarity Radio Show - TEEN SUICIDE PREVENTION SHOW (100519, AUDIO) - https:// tinyurl.com/WAAM-MOC-TeenSuicide]

Back to Veterans again, reach out: 24/7 VA line 855-948-2311

Marten swapped writing instruments again and began comparing his previous notes with what he just read. He made more notes onto the backs of the pages.

Pressures that build up within the fragile human psyche can only be glossed over by humor to a certain degree. Trying to hide from one's feelings can exacerbate a host of already existing physical ailments and can result in a host of stress related disorders of its own. Eventually the lamenting must be dealt with on its own terms, and true healing can only occur when the hurting is alleviated through the shedding of tears and the release of other therapeutic chemicals of the neurological system.

Shock, denial, anger, and in time, eventual acceptance, is defined as the traditional stages in the path of recovery following the death of a loved one. However, these phases are the natural order for more than the loss of life; they hold true, to a lesser degree, in the loss of material possessions as well or the dissolution of a relationship (especially a marriage even when the relationship is not one's own but the separation of parents. That wreaks havoc on anyone's sensibilities). Also, people go through shock, denial, anger, and eventual acceptance when experiencing massive destruction (a fire, flood, or other disaster) or when victims of crime or so many other trials in life that people just do not expect. These sudden events for which people are unprepared are hard to process and put within context of life, living, and dying; the natural order of everyday life; especially the stressors and tension of modern-living.

Being stalled in any one of the steps on the road to recovery can cause long-term damage to the psychological welfare of an individual. Some people can be so overtaken by the shock from the situation that arose in their life that they suffer a complete nervous breakdown. Extended periods of shock can lead to a complete disconnect with reality from which they may never be relieved without professional psychiatric care. Far too many people either cannot seek assistance or just do not seek help with their ability to cope.

While more people have become aware of the psychological route the mind needs to travel in order to heal, so few actually ever gain an insight as to how to deal with each of the stages of the recuperation. Everyone feels alone and isolated on their journey toward mending, especially at first. No one ever taught them how to grieve or how to process these normal junctures of renewal. Friends and relations lack knowledge of how to assist those needing support for their revitalization.

Many people distance themselves out of lack of understanding how to help someone and are afraid of saying the wrong thing, not realizing that there are no real wrong things to say. Just being there is often enough. Allowing the sufferer to understand that their pain is real and natural can help. Providing a sympathetic ear or a shoulder to cry on can ease the process but shying away can add to the overall alienation felt and can lead to further anxiety, depression, stress, and the like.

Anger can manifest itself in several ways, depending on the cause of the grieving process. Physical relief of symptoms may sometimes be required. But being in physical pain certainly does not justify an outburst of violence toward others. There are healthy outlets for burning off added physical energy: jogging, running, playing sports, boxing, cycling, and other physical activities supply a healthy outlet of any potential aggression that a person may not even be aware exists. Such activities also provide much needed interaction with the outside world during their time of suffering, thus offering a dual benefit.

This anger for some, however, is not necessarily aimed at others. Many individuals, rightly or wrongly, blame themselves and try to conceal the resentment they feel about themselves. On the other hand, or by contrast, bullies mask underlying inadequacies in themselves and hope that aggressing upon others somehow will kept bolstering their own esteem or sense of worth. Alternately, for still others, shyness is a coping mechanism as they seek to hide from the world so as to about the things that haunt them in their mind, sometimes they wish they could escape.

Life requires a balance of emotions to survive. Sometimes it takes people longer to cope than others, and the acceptance stage cannot be forced upon anyone. Each individual must reach the plateau on his or her own terms and in his or her own time. Providing honest feedback to a person in torment can aid revival and the return to normalcy. Some, undoubtedly, may temporarily lose the closeness of their friend or family member as the depressed or traumatized person may avoid them as they continue to resist assistance and remain reluctant to move to acceptance.

The distance between a laugh and a good cry, is not a great expanse. Have you ever laughed so hard you began to cry? Conversely, tears can lead to giddiness. It can become present when acceptance is achieved, and we finally adapt. The merriment can often only come if we realize how overly self-important we allowed ourselves to be fooled into.

Humor, for Marten, became a double-edged sword. Indeed, he used it as a deflection at times he feels down. If we don't laugh, we'd be crying as the saying goes. Sometimes we just react; other times we choose how we respond to any given situation.

Marten recalled a visit to his favorite local pizza place near his home, to pick up a pizza on the way home for that night's dinner; giving the family's traditional cook, Hope, a night off. Three young ladies wandered in, two of the three had wild-colored hair and the third was a traditional seemingly natural brunette. Marten's lame sense-of-humor, and desire to never let a "bad-pun" opportunity to pass, immediately took over him. Marten strolled over to their table, and hoping they had good sense of humor; or can appreciate a dose of levity with all the seriousness going on around us all; proceeded to tease them. He complimented the two with the bright red locs and then turned to the third and proclaimed, "you must be the boring one!" Thankfully, they chuckled. He let them know he was very happy that they took his comments in the spirit they were intended, all in good fun. His name was called, and as he left, he imparted them with one last thought: "remember, things could always be better, but they could often be worse!"

He smiled the entire way home. He felt he had indeed made these young ladies' day a bit brighter; without a clue whether they needed the uplifting or not.

Marten recalled the verse that says, "love your neighbor, as yourself," and he certainly knew he welcomed the kindness of strangers. While an odd one, he knew his jovial comments were a bit of a random act of kindness in a loose sense, a good deed. He recalled the verse in Matthew too: "you shall know them by their fruits!" Contextually applicable beyond the negative connotation about misdeeds, but too those who engage in good deeds. Alas, Marten thought, so many love to tout only certain scripture while at times completely overlooking other relevant passages that provide context, a clarification, an extension, of other life lessons of religious texts. There is far more to Ephesians 1:7 "In Him we have redemption through His blood, the forgiveness of sins, according to the riches of His grace" and much beyond that is still expected of Christians. Again, be "Brother's Keeper" clearly commands an action from us (not deferring it to government), a deed, a task, at test of own personal worthiness by that which we afford others. These things also tenants of other religions and their texts too.

It is important to act like a person of faith and not just tell people you are one, in Marten's belief. Don't just spout Scripture and expect a nonbeliever to fall to their knees and join the faith. Show your beliefs with your actions, don't just tell people. He chuckled aloud, momentarily thinking about the Canadian Rock group Rush's *Show Don't Tell* tune. Don't just wear a cross necklace. Act like the One who hung on the cross for your sins. Only then verbalize *the Word* when they are open to hearing it and ready for their next step toward redemption.

So, yes, humor is important. Faithful words of encouragement too. His book would be a multiple-front mission. He was called to write this book and would give glory to God in it. He would be a Christian messenger but not an overbearing one so-as to not have someone tune-out from the message having been too aggressive.

10

MADRID, SPAIN

THE TRAIN IS A SMALL WORLD
MOVING THROUGH A LARGER WORLD.

—Elisha Cooper

*S*pain's 2004 elections were first and foremost in the minds of Madrid residents, and their focus would soon put the entire city, and subsequently the country, into a state of fear, panic, and suspicion.

For the majority of locals, however, the day was just as any other. It was time to begin to prepare for another workday. Time to prepare the children for their school day. Another list of errands to be run and accomplished, such as a grocery shopping list, picking up laundry, or meeting a friend for lunch. People were going about their mundane everyday daily life, not appreciating being alive. They were going through the motions rather than savoring a great day, life, love, opportunity. There were breakfasts to be made, lunches to be packed, and tight schedules to be followed.

The ebb and flow of Madrid, like many large metropolitan cities, revolved around a delicate balance of private and commuter transportation carriers. While the average family, just like in America, would always prefer to the flexibility of owning their own vehicle, many opt for the predictability and ease of the commuter trains.

Adding to their daily concerns was the stress of getting to the voting booth and who to vote for—who might actually improve their lives. Many longed for a swing toward more freedoms and less government meddling as too much of the trend all across the globe has been toward control and more mandates, more demands that people sacrifice in the name of the greater good, which now means having more and more confiscated from the productive and redistributed to others. It's like they want fewer and fewer people pulling the cart and more freeloaders riding in the cart.

The elections, not terrorism, was the predominant concern, but those who hate calm and instead prefer people be in a constant state of chaos had other plans. They had been calculating their line of attack for some time, and it was time to strike.

There were three million residents, nine percent of total, packed into the center of the Iberian Peninsula that encompasses the Spanish city. It was not only the focus of political power but of the nation's economic stability as well. The GIJIAS like striking political targets as well as economic ones, which made Madrid the perfect dual opportunity.

Amidst the cafes and Terrazas, El rastro flea markets, bars, clubs, discos were large influxes of development cash from the European Union. It was one of several host cities for 1992 cultural events, a 2012 Olympics bid, and was very attractive to tourists. Terrorists also hold dear the chance to strike multiple persuasions of Westerners at once. Again, Madrid was an added bonus if you will for such a bull's eye mark.

The Madrilenian rail system had become a model for European travel. It is a prototypical of high-capacity efficiency that begged, in some terrorists' minds, for an attack. Its precision of operations made planning easier and aiding the surprise among the complacent and their sense of "good-times" about to be molested.

On March 11, 2004, a new infamous date was added and "3/11" would soon become as synonymous as "9/11" in the terrorist calendar—another key commemoration to forever be weary of. It turned out to be the deadliest attack against civilians on European soil since the 1988 Lockerbie, Scotland, airliner bombing.

Like the Tokyo plot, the terrorists made this a bit of a copy-cat attack, minus the poison-gas, and deployed assault teams to multiple trains. When all was said and done, a total of ten cellphone-controlled IEDs backpack bombs devasted four separate trains.

Beyond just Madrid's Atocha station, the terrorists killed passengers near El Poso del Tio Raimundo and Santa Eugenia. Three other bombs were later discovered undetonated, saving countless lives and others from being maimed. Those bombs left behind invaluable clues for investigators to help later track down the perpetrators.

Area hospitals became inundated with injured Spaniards, as the estimated final count of those wounded topped two thousand. First responders were stretched thin, an obvious consideration of the attack plan. They hit several places, overloaded rescue systems, and sent law enforcement into a tizzy having to reserve forces for potential secondary attacks that could occur, and the inevitable reports from anxious people about backpacks elsewhere.

If a backpack owner could not be identified, authorities were supposed to cordon off the perimeter to protect those in proximity. The Atlanta Olympics bombing came to mind. Richard Jewel spotted a backpack and called first responders to engage in protocol, but the IED detonated before a sufficient radius of protection could be formed.

In that instance, the FBI quickly labeled Richard Jewel as a person of interest. They thought Jewel planted the bomb and then reported it so as to fulfill a hero complex. They had seen such a scenario before by someone craving attention.

Richard Jewel was eventually cleared of all charges. And for many years a sense of terror remained around Atlanta, which is understandable when a killer remains on the loose and as the Atlanta attack went unsolved for so long afterward.

Fortunately, in Madrid, within a few months, after another failed attempt at a bombing, two-dozen suspects were rounded up and most were convicted. The suspected ringleader, however, was acquitted due to lack of sufficient prosecutable evidence.

11

LONDON, UK

ONE DAY MEN WILL LOOK BACK AND SAY
I GAVE BIRTH TO THE TWENTIETH CENTURY.

—Jack the Ripper

*T*he nation with the strictest gun control laws is a haven for stabbings. England seems to have ensured the legacy of Jack the Ripper would remain. A very long return list of his victims can be easily obtained via an internet search. England seems to be proud of his legacy and ensures it endures and its citizens unable to defend themselves!

Marten jotted down just a few brief notes for further investigation. He wanted to be sure to include a chapter in *Terrorist Tracks* throughout the United Kingdom, or at least the terrorist attacks in and around London, and there were many from which to choose.

Unsuspecting motorists and pedestrians around London bridge in 2017 became the targets of three men in a van that tried hitting as many as possible. Then, not satisfied with the mayhem they produced and uncertain they may have actually killed anyone, they abandoned the van and moved on foot to the Burough Market area and began to randomly stab market goers in order to maximize the terror and potential casualties they could inflict.

Certainly not the only vehicular homicide attempt. Many wannabe terrorists all over the globe would copy over the decades. One recent one took place was at a Christmas parade in Waukesha, Wisconsin. A man in an SUV pulled onto the thoroughfare where the celebration was taking place and struck participants and onlookers. Eyewitnesses reported that he steered wildly, swerving back and forth, not to avoid people as if he had accidentally turned onto a busy street, but clearly in an effort to maximize the numbers of people he could hit, wound, and possibly kill.

Darrell Brooks was later apprehended in Wisconsin. Brooks had recently been released from prison on the latest progressive "no cash bail" craze for trying to kill another person with his vehicle. If he been held for attempted murder in that case, the Christmas parade incident would have been avoided.

Marten thought about the whole "defund the police" and "no bail" movements of heavily Democrat run cities. Prosecutors were out-right refusing to bring charges against many criminals and letting them right back out onto the streets to offend again. Predictable, when you go soft on crime, crime soars. Once again it would have to be a topic for someone else to make a much needed deep-dive book release. No study would need to be conducted; it is obvious to anyone with an ounce of common sense, as it is playing out in major cities and not just in America where such liberal policies are being implemented.

In London, crackdowns on any weapon does not stop them. Instead, the criminals adapt to other weapons. Without guns, assaults do not subside, just the method by which the assailants engage in attacks. In 2017 there began an escalation on the series of knife attacks. Should they be declared assault knives and be banned, then a new rash of baseball bat outbreaks would begin.

Just two years later, in 2019 there was another terrorist stabbing spree. Usman Khan brandished two blades. He succeeded in penetrating and killing two bystanders before being shot by police while resisting arrest and exposing a terror vest. Fearing that Khan would detonate and create a much larger mass-casualty situation, the law-enforcement officers that were armed with firearms, fired and killed him. The vest was then discovered to be a fake. It was concluded he just wanted to kill himself in what is known today as suicide by cop—the martyrdom (murder-suicide) mentality.

The next year would be no better. The reckless wielding of blades went on relentlessly. Sudesh Amman stole a knife from a store and proceeded to wound two. Like Khan in 2019, Amman wore a fake murder-suicide vest and therefore was shot on the scene and expired.

Marten came across an attack event that the perpetrators were not happy with just stabbing their victims. They planned an assault on a British soldier with even greater malice. Like one, yes there were several, of the London bridge assaults, Michael Adebolajo and Michael Adebowale, claiming to be soldiers of Allah, vehicularly mowed down Lee Rigby outside his base. They then proceeded to stab him with a knife. That not being sufficient, in their mind, escalated and hacked him to death with a cleaver.

Just how in-depth Marten thought he would need to get in such a chapter, as with other chapters dealing with factual information, he was not sure. Readers would not likely appreciate a dramatization of such a bloody attack – if they want blood, guts spilling, and other gore, they could see any number of horror films. He thought it best to spare his readers scenes of such in his book probably the best approach. A cursory mention of all the battered and bloodied innocent people, having committed no offense toward their attackers to warrant the unprovoked hatred, gushing blood, desperate for aid in stopping the hemorrhaging, sufficient. Sometimes less is more. His readers would get the point and would likely be able to imagine how painful it must be to be stabbed with a sharp object and then wondering if help would be able to arrive in time to prevent bleeding out to death.

It would indeed be a brief chapter, leaving room for more detailed accounts of other attacks. He would just write informatively, from a historical perspective. It would be a warning much in the vein of Nostradamus; he might deal in such things as survivor's guilt and other important concepts.

War and Peace was already a thing if people wanted to seek out such a long read. Though he considered referencing Sun Tzu's *Art of War* as well as several other more recent materials detailing the modern terrorist's mindset toward guerrilla warfare, supplements to his book, as well as other classics that still relate to all the violence and desires of some for military conquest.

There was more, however, that had to be addressed.

Terror in England was certainly not limited to these narrow effectiveness blade assaults. Britain had been a high target and many assaults had occurred before these, but most notably were ones after

9/11. The world changed so much following 9/11. Terror cells all over clearly became emboldened and inspired that such a large blow had taken place.

March 2017, there were yet another set of vehicular manslaughter in Westminster. There was another vehicle crossing a bridge. This one was the Westminster bridge, and the terrorist hit as many pedestrians as he could. Often, terrorists lack imagination; they generally fall into copy-cat patterns and so the general public is saved then far greater catastrophic events.

Back in 2005 there was the 7/7 offensive. Terrorists love dates that will capture the imagination. Hundreds were scarred in another well calculated and executed action upon multiple targets. A total of fifty-two people were killed that day as terrorists disbursed to three stations of London's underground, and another attacker was deployed to an above ground point; another link in the mass-transit of commuters' chain.

The attack came at a time when many Englanders were still celebrating the Olympics being awarded to London for, distant at that point, 2012. The attackers had plotted for some time and moved up their date of attack after the Olympic announcement, rightly suspecting that Londoners guards would then be down while they were distracted with the good news.

The three underground stations were struck almost simultaneously just before nine a.m. With the secondary strike on the bus almost exactly sixty minutes later.

Marten recalled this assault. The televisions had been filled with horrific video of billowing smoke, people desperately trying to aid the wounded, all while uncertain if additional attempts were planned to kill still more on that June 2005 morning. It burned deep into Marten's memory as indeed one of the more well-planned and well-executed, more complex, attacks involving a significant crew size.

So many reports of suspicious activity go unreported that could prevent an attack. Like that of the San Bernadino, California assault. Threats had been made, and neighbors testified after the fact that they suspected something was up, but they feared to be the one to try to expose clear likely terrorist criminality ahead of an attack, and embarrassment if they were wrong. Conversely, officials get so many unsubstantiated reports that tie up investigators time; sometimes they are unwarranted prejudice influenced. Meanwhile, those who need to be surveilled manage to elude scrutiny and evade capture that would prevent them from acting upon their acts of terror or aiding and abetting others that could have exposed a plot and been nipped in the bud.

As was one other case, with an IED like the Boston Bombers and the Atlanta Olympics Village bomber, one was packed with shrapnel and detonated outside the Manchester arena following an Ariana Grande concert. Marten remembered that one splashed all over the news for days also. Twenty-two people, including children who attended the concert with their parents, were killed and many more were severely injured by the blast. Inside, people were trampled when confusion and panic ensued near the arena exit, as the detonation occurred while the majority of the crowd had not made it out the exits yet.

The Wuhan virus seems to in no way shape or form slowed down those conspiring to kill. The national news outlet reported that in the virus years, six plans were foiled in England alone. That total soars to thirty-one, looking at just the year preceding the pandemic period.

The pandemic, quite the opposite of deterring terrorism, caused terrorists to focus on a different target set. The virus, while reducing potential aims of terrorists in some locations, meant that other locations stayed full. While people stayed home, attackers targeted apartment complexes and the like. Maniacal fanatics do not rest. These established terrorists, and some terrorist wannabe types who had more opportunity to be further radicalized online during their confinements, grew the terrorist pool.

Evil never rests; it only adapts and shifts, finds new opportunities. They believe the virus was a distraction from their messaging. Their need for terror to be unstopping. Likewise, though, they would see the post-pandemic period as ripe for larger assaults. People having been distracted, lack of reporting on attacks that did occur during the lockdowns creating a complacency, perhaps now lulled into another false sense of security. A return to the "9/10" mindset likely among large sectors of the populace.

Marten's eyes grew tired from making notes on his printed pages and staring at the screen for more information was wearing on him. A quick glance at the clock and encroaching lateness, now seemed a good time for another sleeping pill and retire to bed. It seemed that maybe he was getting sidetracked on other books and started going down the whole history of war and terrorism rabbit hole. If he could lose those thoughts enough to doze off, hopefully too the nightmares would grant him a reprieve tonight.

He needed a good night's sleep. He'd been dragging for days. Countless nights disrupted. Countless cups of coffee in desperate attempts to keep going. This was, no doubt, taking a large toll on his health, and Hope was concerned that he might be developing greater ailment from the stress and lack of sound sleep.

12

HELL ON EARTH

THE WICKED SHALL BE TURNED INTO HELL,
AND ALL THE NATIONS THAT FORGET GOD.

—Psalm 9:17

ell on earth exists, and while many consider it to be Detroit, it's not. Detroit, the butt of many jokes in Michigan, falls to a close second. In fact, the more notorious Hell, Michigan, became, the greater the nickname "not quiet Hell, but damn close" began to stick to Detroit.

Many are unaware that Detroit is actually just south of Canada, well south of Windsor Ontario Canada anyway. You can go south to Canada or can both experience Paradise and Hell in Michigan—by car, in the same day!

Forget "Yes, Virginia, there is a Santa Clause." Whether you are religious or not think "Yes Charity, Hell exists." Hell, incarnate lives just sixty miles west of Detroit and about thirty miles north of Devil's Lake. Nestled in its own Bermuda (a.k.a. Devil's) Triangle of

Michigan freeways I-94, I-96, and M-50. A town that lives each day as if it were the last, the horror noir capital of the world welcomes its most important calendar day each year: Halloween. However, 2006 presented its greatest opportunity and catapulted Hell to new heights. With the appearance of 06/06/06 on the celestial horizon, Hell became more than a Michigan phenomenon. It shot to global significance.

The Detroit media, and other outlets looking for occasional playful stories far afield of the usual crime and punishment runs, were quick to play it up. Hell, Michigan, was a central player to that fact. June 6, 2006 – 6/6/6 – was tailor made for a horrific event. That year was the pinnacle because it also included the debut of the latest incarnation of the horror film *The Omen*. The new film was ready to hit the screen in Hell, and they had a weeklong festival to commemorate the event.

Hell, the city, unlike the lake of fire or Dante's layers of suffering, is actually a rather nice and fun place. Folks who visit the lower peninsula Michigan location find wonderful places to eat, nice gift shops, and a mini-golf course. Most important, you'll want to let your friends and family know this is the only Hell you ever intend to experience. While at one of the gift shops buy some post cards. Scribble anything on them. The main thing is that you can then wander to the post office and have your postcards post marked and delivered from the bowels of Hell.

Do not be shocked when a gift shop clerk pulls out a lighter and adds a touch of authenticity by lightly burning the corners to show that it did indeed spend time in Hell. It's a fun place with a sense of humor, not persecution.

Marten thought for sure that his FBI friend Nicholas Anderson would have had something about the terror threat level. Why else would he want to meet him? Would Nic provide some candid insight or was that going to be too much to expect? What, Marten wondered, would be lurking about that Nic would want a conversation? The same week as the 666 controversy. Alas, no, but then Marten thought a bit more about it.

The truth is, the GIJIAS would never want to be associated with this date. On the contrary, these 666 notions are a heavily Christian related notion. To associate any attack with 666 would jeopardize the very notion of the jihad being a "just and noble" cause. Linking it with a demonic tone would just further connect them with evil incarnate, as many moral people already did, and for good reason. But anything anywhere around such a date and any linking with the new anti-Christ and an alliance with the Devil would just be giving the West a gift to further demonize them.

Quite to the contrary, the GIJIAS consider America, and other Western nations, to be the Great Satan – Israel the Little Satan puppet. To detract from this point of view, would be a great disservice to their cause. The ability to recruit weak-minded individuals to their cause depends, to a large degree, on being able to continue that rhetoric.

Islamic extremist fundamentalists would dare not stir that hornet nest even among its most ardent sympathizers. They would just pick another date. There are plenty of others. So, the day came and went without incident.

Well, without terrorist incident. They partied in Hell like it was *1999* as musical artist Prince would say. Partying like A BEAST on SIX-SIX-SIX was certainly a better marketing angle, and they played it up for all it was worth. The restaurants were packed; the bars were packed; it was green-to-green people on the min-golf course. The gift shops were restocking racks and shelves with "Route 666" and "Hell, Michigan" paraphernalia, along with a host of other appropriately marked shirts. A record numbers of post cards were "toasted." The Hell Post Office had never had as much mail to have to post mark.

Marten had many friends in politics, and he often wondered why they wouldn't take the marketing coup they would likely reap by visiting Hell to launch a Michigan-based campaign. Marten had suggested to a few the marketing slogan: "I am the candidate willing to go to Hell and back for you" from a podium in Hell, Michigan. Politics is serious business, but sometimes you have to show you are a regular guy or gal and just have a little fun.

Marten himself, had zero political aspirations. He was very happy working behind the scenes, and being a journalist, he needed to maintain at least a façade of neutrality. He figured if his becoming an author was indeed successful and they were able to move to a more rural location, then he would become more involved. Becoming an actual party delegate was an important part of the process. One can scream and complain from the bleachers as much as they like, if one does not become a delegate and part of the processes, one will never, ever have any chance at shaping the outcome on the field. One must suit up, take the field, and make some plays in order to help the team become better, however one might define such.

After a visit to Hell, you can drive just three hundred thirty-eight miles north into the Upper Peninsula of Michigan and spend some recovery time in Paradise, Michigan. Personally, Marten thought they should change their name to Heaven to market to visitors a Heaven and Hell trip. Why the two separate "Chamber of Commerce" members for both would not team up for such, is beyond him.

Many states have their unique immigrant enclaves: Chinatown, Little Italy, Little Havana. Properly immigrated peoples have had great benefit and support moving to such enclaves. Marten thought about the topic of immigration and the difference between legal immigrants he gladly welcomed and had many interactions with versus illegal immigrants and the border invasion—and all the political fire around it.

Marten quickly put that out of his mind though as yet another topic or rabbit hole for his nom de plume online blog publications, not for this book to deal with. What would also matter to his readers, however, would be another unique city in Michigan: Dearborn. If you visit Dearborn, you'll likely see Allen Park and the home of the Detroit Lions, but they are always a sore subject. He always said it wasn't the Lions but the Ford family ownership that caused the curse – oh how he wishes they would sell to someone that would really build the franchise. Once a decade, and only once a decade, they would look like they may finally turn a corner. Then, yes, the inevitable Lionsesque collapse.

At any rate, Dearborn was what mattered immensely following 9/11. The microscope was focused on Dearborn – the good, the bad, and the ugly. One of the greats in Marten's mind was his favorite Italian restaurant: Roman Village.

While Dearborn Michigan is the actual home to the Ford Motor company headquarters, it is also sometimes referred to as Little Arabia for its largest Arab population within the United States. Following 9/11 those who didn't know about Dearborn quickly learned of it.

Would Dearborn become a flashpoint of hate or one of healing? It all depended upon who you asked. Security certainly needed to be stepped up for the entire area until Dearborners and Detroiters showed the world they could and do get along as Arabs, non-Arabs, Christians, Jews, and Muslims. Oh sure, there was an occasional bit of trouble but nothing like some thought might erupt.

Any and every sub-group maintains varying aspects of their own culture, but America as a melting pot generally proved to be a success – including the Dearborn conglomeration of diverse peoples. Until the age of identity politics when modern fascism came into being and certain people made both their money and ability to use such for power and control. When immigrants escaping tyranny abroad legally came to the United States with a true desire to become American, there were little issues.

What mattered was the clear message to the United States and the rest of the world following 9/11, racism has no place anywhere, and wherever it is allowed to fester bad developments would likely arise over time as tensions build. No one race is any better than another. No one race has a lock on goodness, morality, or on always getting their way despite all the woke white privilege talk. Nor is any one race all bad, and sadly still so many want to peddle such 'Bigotry of low expectations' upon others 'not them' stereotypes.

Criminals exist in the ranks of all groups. Wonderful role models and heroes do too. History, when accurately told, shows many great accomplishments among all sorts of peoples. There is often more to any story. Don't believe those who peddle hate and division for political gain.

Sadly, it is not just GIJIAS that play up our differences to try to invoke mistrust and hatred, to play on the emotions, rather than logic and reason, of people. The "Facts Don't Care About Your Feelings" meme is popular on social media. The bad people play up suspicions in order to gain or maintain a degree of power and control for themselves. They keep the masses at odds, fighting each other, hopped up with emotional catalysts, within nations, rather than focusing on the real enemies. Those who wish to control others rule over every aspect of peoples' lives; it's antithetical to the American dream and America's constitutional republic foundations.

Failed ideologies of communism and fascism are resurfacing and allowing for the already rich and powerful to remain such, while others made to do with less, expected to have lower expectations. Ruling elites always do well; the enslaved masses not so much. Would be leaders always promise heaven, but their policies, despite their supposed good intentions, only delivery hell on earth – and not the fun kind found in Hell, Michigan.

13

THE PYRAMID

WHEN WE FIND SOMETHING NEW AT GIZA, WE ANNOUNCE
IT TO THE WORLD. THE SPHINX AND THE PYRAMIDS ARE
WORLD TREASURES. WE ARE THE GUARDIANS OF THESE
TREASURES, BUT THEY BELONG TO THE WORLD.

—Zahi Hawass

*H*ope agreed to a research trip or two as part of Marten's book project. So, when Nic wanted a face-to-face meeting in Nevada, Hope conceded to the hastily scheduled trip. It was a chance to get away; as the Go Go's tune attests; and seriously get into his research and run some ideas by Nic to get some insights and direction for the manuscript. It was a chance to be away from all the distractions of home. Most important, Nic might have something juicy to tell him.

Marten booked the next flight out for a Sunday through Thursday getaway. Marten and Hope hadn't been to the area for several years. Nevada, and either Vegas or Laughlin, was a usual vacation destination every few years for Marten, Hope, and the kids. Their usual outings avoided the weekends as the resorts were far more eager to give a deal to those willing to stay the weekdays.

For Marten and his crew, it was a chance to see all the changes. There were always old properties being shuttered and torn down to make way for newer more extravagant properties, or massive remodels of aging but still able to attract a tourists-based properties. No matter how many times he'd been there, the area was always reinventing itself in some way. There were always new sights and shows to see or a recurring one missed last time out, and whether or not there would be a new roller coaster or not the old ones were a must ride every trip.

The weekends were full of people traveling in from California and other nearby states ready to play craps and blackjack, so the casinos didn't really need to offer incentives. The airlines retained their higher fares for people who really wanted to be somewhere for a weekend as they usually were willing to pay a premium. So, the Sunday through Thursday outings provided great discounts and allowed for more of the vacation budget to be spent on side trips, shows, gambling, and other fun pursuits. Marten still intended to get some pleasure from this expedition, but the primary focus was business.

During the flight Marten pondered the ever-changing scenery of America as he floated across the land. He always looked forward to catching a glimpse of the wonderous St. Louis Arch marking the gateway to the west, and this trip out brought the recollection of the relevant previous terror threats made against it. He watched the endless fields of crops give way to the Grand Canyon, and finally the southern jag and descent into LAS. It was a majestic beauty you only experience in North America. Sure, Europe had its wonderful sights and landmarks, but Marten always felt so renewed seeing this magnificence of God's creation of his homeland.

Upon touchdown at Las Vegas International, Marten called Nic, pretending it was just a happenstance visit between two old friends. They never knew who might be listening. As he exited the terminal and into the ninety-plus-degree dry breeze, it actually was a welcome feeling. Michigan had been the grip of humid heat wave. While Michigan is certainly not a tropical location, its proximity to so much fresh water made it as bad as Key West some summer days.

Marten packed light, so he could carry-on his bag and avoid luggage claims to get in and out of the airport quickly, something that certainly was not an option on the family trips. Those always comprised of several, heavy rolling luggage bags. This time, he was very thankful to be quickly off to the car rental agency and then a fairly short transit to Laughlin. Marten welcomed these drives. He loved getting out of Detroit and into the wonderful different sand and rock landscape, and, yes, he loved seeing the many colorful casinos along the thoroughfares.

The rental agency had his usual GMC Envoy waiting under the club canopy, tucked away from the blaze of the sun's burning gaze. Marten always rented Envoys as they afforded a certain aspect of comfort for his somewhat larger frame, and they provided an added piece of mind that he would be able to work around any road conditions, or even off-road capabilities. The Envoy was gassed and ready, as always; he powered the vehicle to life and drove off into the clear day. The weather was lovely, as long as you had sunscreen, hat, shades, and air-conditioning. The dry heat was welcoming, but still nothing he wanted to be out in for too long.

The short drive down Tropicana to the freeway system was bumper to bumper as usual. Traffic in and around the Vegas Strip was always packed, except for the emptiness all experienced a bit of time following 9/11. The Vegas Strip was empty then, and one could linger on the roadway along the New York New York casino where so many stopped to lay 9/11 tribute items for the fallen and the first-responder heroes near the resort's mini-Statue of Liberty.

The time passed quickly as he took in the view coming off the main freeways and onto the lessor highway system navigation routes. He pulled into the Pyramid driveway toward the magnificent structure.

The Pyramid Casino and Resort was located at the south extremity of the Laughlin strip along the Colorado River. Its gleaming bronze exterior was designed to mimic the sandstone of the pyramids in Egypt, and its high-powered lights beamed its rotating radiance from its apex into the Nevada nights like a lighthouse, though they called people to come rather than avoid the lights.

The Colorado River itself provided a lovely site as it streamed from the Rocky Mountains, weaving through the Grand Canyon, flowing passed the Laughlin strip and on down to the Sea of Cortez. Marten anticipated a chance at a leisurely walk along the mile-long Riverwalk and, weather permitting, perhaps further north along the trails beyond. A potential quick riverboat run offer him a chance to be out on the water and enjoy the cooling breezes, even if it might be a short ride due to the shallow places along the approximately quarter-mile wide section.

Another riverboat obstacle, the Davis Dam makes use of the Colorado River to generate electricity just three and a half miles to the north. The dam was completed in the 1950s and like its bigger brother the Hoover Dam is not the only great wonder American building know how of man over nature to provide for its practical need to help provide much needed energy and clean water for the region. The workers at the "little brother" dam would never admit to an inferiority complex. Big brother Hoover may indeed be bigger, but Davis is equally important to regional survival.

While in Laughlin Marten wanted to try to grab a trip back to the Don Laughlin's Classic Car Museum. The auto collection there rivals the collection at the former Imperial Palace on the Vegas strip. On his way into Laughlin Marten took Christmas Tree Pass; he knew it was a bit silly, not flashy like one expects out of all things Nevada, but as a Christian, it held an enduring place in his heart. Plus, it gave him a chance to stretch the legs at Grapevine Canyon and view again the hundreds of ancient petroglyphs carved into the rocky granite landscape.

Upon arriving at the Pyramid, Marten handed off his vehicle to the valet, gathered his carry-on bag and laptop carrier, and headed into the massive formation. Parts of the beautiful grounds around the Pyramid mimicked an Egyptian excavation site while other parts were lavish gardens, patios, and walkways with mummies awaiting you at the main entrance, and, of course, the gift shop. Nevada isn't just about gambling anymore; it is about the whole experience and hoping you'll buy things to take back home to share your experience with others. Gifts and great eateries were every bit as important as the casinos to the area's commercial success. Across from the gift shop was a lavishly ornated lobby with Egyptian gods carved into the ornate front desk.

Entering the Pyramid was like walking into another world, as if walking onto a sci-fi set for a *Stargate SG-1* episode or transporting to an Egyptian archeological dig. Pausing to take in the awesome obelisks and other massive compositions adorning ancient hieroglyphical texts, Marten pondered if they'd gone so far as to carve actual Egyptian writings into the monoliths or if they were purely decoration.

Just a bit more into the interior the Dig-site mateam; Arabic for restaurant; with the world-renowned buffet on one side and a more traditional family-style seating restaurant on the other. Marten was eager to have a tasty, but fairly expensive, dinner as the days of cheap eats at Nevada casinos had long vanished. They were mostly higher end eateries with big-named chefs proudly displayed on the marquees that attract their own following. After check-in, Marten took a quick trip up to his room to drop off his bag and laptop and then he was on his way to allow his taste buds to savor a juicy steak. After dinner he planned on a little blackjack at the five-dollar table; he was never a big gambler. He and Hope rarely visited the casinos in Detroit. Just for entertainment they would have a trip to the buffet, brief use of the one-arm-bandits, and if all went well, they would walk out with about the same amount of money they went in with. Hitting the jackpot would be nice, but Marten saw hanging about and spending with reckless abandon until achieving such as not sensible and never part of his budget. Everything in moderation was his motto. Yet another part of Marten's practical side.

His mind wandered as he again took in the views. He was amazed at the modern marvels of American know how, though for some that was an issue. The Pyramid provided an example of American decadence and capitalism to the Islamic fundamentalist mindset.

Many too with a socialist mindset, including modern American fascists, have a warped sense of the ideology as history has all but erased the evils of the Nazi's and Il Duce acolytes, who were also socialists. There were some differences but not some wild, completely new divergence of existing political systems. Many spoiled brats in America not understanding how lucky they are to have been born here. The grass is always greener on the other side, so they think. To American leftists, rather than see these things as great tributes, an homage, and monuments to American cultural diversity, something they often tout and are hypocritical in this regard, American welcoming and acceptance and celebration, a great melting pot of all peoples and blending of cultures, instead to them it is an afront as 'cultural appropriation' flagrantly on display. The only thing that GIJIAS loved about America was that among all the self-loathing American leftists it was easy for them to hide. Sometimes they even gained their favor in their destructive efforts.

The Pyramid Casino and Resort as a replica of the very shape, a copy, of the great Egyptian pyramids represents to the GIJIAS America's greed as denoted by the all-seeing eye above the incomplete pyramid on the reverse of the United States one dollar bill. These identifications within the American mindset, as the terrorist viewed it, made the Pyramid a key target as an additional; further western assault on September 11th 2001, or potential other future attack. Just as one hijacker used the Hudson River as a guide into one of the Twin Towers that fateful day, a hijacker could straddle the Colorado River as a guide into the Pyramid.

Las Vegas itself, known as "Sin City," and Laughlin only a slightly lessor degree, having become perceived as the gambling "mecca;" of course the term alone used, rather in the terrorist mindset, appropriated and misused; of the world. It is considered even more licentious than Morocco or Beirut prior to its destruction through years of Arab and Israeli conflict and subsequent civil wars. Atlantic City and Laughlin were deemed the Little Sin Cities just as GIJIAS referred to the United States as the Big Satan and Israel as the Little Satan. All through the GIJIAS dictionary of rhetoric such parallels always existed.

After his very filling dinner, Marten played a little bit at the tables. He was up and down but luckily left only down twenty bucks before heading up to his room. He was by no means a great card player, but at least he knew the basic rules and to avoid any table with a wild-eyed first-timer looking to hit on seventeen when the dealer was likely sitting at twelve. "Let the dealer bust," he would scream in his head. Once settled into his room, Marten decided on an early morning Riverwalk stroll to see what may have changed from the last time he was there on a family trip.

The next morning Marten noted minor changes and updates to the buildings. Nevada was ever changing, which was part of its allure. The Laughlin strip had its many familiar spots, but there were a lot of changes in store for Marten's stroll. The sidewalks were busier than his visit in the spring following the 9/11 terrorist attacks, but they were still eerily quieter than the normal hustle and bustle. The sparseness of the walkways was unusual considering the growth of the accommodations about the Laughlin Colorado River strip. The people would still be spread across the same stretch that connected the influx of people into Laughlin from their originating points.

He wasn't staying in Vegas, but his mind drifted back to thoughts of the New York New York Hotel and Casino that had become a gravitational point for all in Vegas after the 9/11 attacks still had its increased sense of patriotic value. Everyone still wanted to be a part of the experience there, as if it were an actual trip to the Big Apple, as New York city had become known over the years, itself. Every inch of the fence line after 9/11 had become a makeshift memorial to those who had so tragically lost their lives to the insanity of the September madness.

The dedications inked onto T-shirts, ribbons, yard signs, and just about any other material one could mark with support for the loved ones of the NYPD and the NYFD, Port authority, and all the other agencies that had so valiantly sent assistance into the WTC area while trying to evacuate the general public from the scene, were strewn about the "NY NY" casino property. For years these commemorations were to remain respectfully untouched. Marten knew the love would not last forever, but he wished it lasted longer than it did. He would have passed the New York New York if he'd been in Vegas. Sadly, there was no Laughlin equivalent. Even if there had been such a display then, like in Vegas, the support and monuments to "never forget" would have been long cleared by now.

The links between properties seemed to diminish even more as the name of the game continued to progress more toward making better use of capturing and keeping people upon your own mega estate. While this strategy was never abandoned by the controlling interests of casino owners, they recognized visitors were wandering from the reservations to view and sample the offerings of the competitors. They adjusted by creating additional attractions of their own in an attempt to hold the tourists spending even along the connect ways to within the confines of their cash registers. Laughlin was more condensed than the Vegas strip, which finally conceded to visitors by offering newer trams and creating elevated crosswalks to make it easier to get around the Vegas strip. The Laughlin Riverwalk remained sufficient for tourists.

Comps, or complimentary amenities, were still a major tool used to monopolize tourists' money. The new incarnation of the comp had evolved into just a series of inexpensive giveaways or discounted services. "Buy one get one free" offers abounded if you'd register for the onsite perks program and loyalty card. Comps consisted of an occasional free meal, show, or night's stay, but the reality is, if you gambled long enough to earn the comps, you would have usually more than paid the full price it would have otherwise cost you to just purchase the goods or services. By giving you something that cost them little or nothing, they are able to make you feel like one of their very important persons. Lumpit the trumpet guy was going to be paid to play whether it was to a full or empty concert or showroom house of people anyway, and for public relations purposes alone they did not want empty theaters reflecting negatively on their offerings. People are social. They don't want to celebrate alone. A crowded theater adds to their experience. Word of an empty theater is negative publicity, and the casino would do whatever possible to avoid such.

During the leaner years immediately after 9/11, Nevadan's adjusted to maintain revenue streams despite the reduced stream of tourists, and they kept up the illusion of crowds dispel any notion that their land was the newest Nevada ghost town. Ghost town would, of course, been a little harsh, but seasoned Nevada travelers knew the difference. For some, that drove in from the surrounding states while flights in were rarer, it seemed a welcomed adjustment, so the die was cast. A silent, self-delusion of great proportions. They were so glad that it only took a few years of scaled back operations before the elbow-to-elbow crowds returned.

Marten was supposed to meet Nic at eleven a.m. at Dig-site mateam for breakfast. Marten arrived fifteen minutes early to begin drinking coffee and ensuring an alert, awake, and open mind for whatever Nic would discuss. This would not be an open meeting with notepad and pen. Marten would have to take everything down mentally and off the record.

After only a few sips into Marten's coffee Nic settled into the booth across from his friend and raised his index finger to convey to Marten to wait a minute. He reached into his suit coat with his left hand. Marten knew immediately he was in for something important. This motion meant only one thing. Nic was switching on a communications scrambler.

While the casinos had their own security measures to block and scramble some communication, so as to deter would be cheaters who might be using electronic devices or the cell phone in the gaming areas, Nic took security to the next level. Marten hadn't realized Nic had paid the staff to ensure no one was sitting within earshot. It even took a while for Marten to realize that his friend's actions of wiping his mouth with a napkin, raising up the newspaper in between them, and other gestures were not rude. Marten had no inkling as to the nature of the week's events that were unfolding the very same day of his arrival.

Marten was at first befuddled with Nic's indirect references and vagueness, beyond his normal candidness or lack thereof. Marten figured out that this Monday mornings news developments consisted of a potential Toronto 17, as they were first thought; later it was determined that it was a group of fourteen adults and four youth whose terrorist plot was thwarted. There had always been Canadian cells, but they were mostly deemed as launching pads to threats within the confines of the United States. Now it was possible that the Prime Minister of Canada and its Parliament had been touted as targets again. While Marten had been acting like a tourist, the North American continent was on the defensive against major developments in the War on Terror. Canada was shocked into reality with the Toronto 18, and now again a fundamentalists copycat group was a threat.

Nic informed Marten he would likely be able to give him the low down in the morning. "Same time, same place?" he suggested.

Marten nodded and went back to his coffee. So far this is not at all what he was expecting to hear. At least he would be free to head over to the car collection and had enough time to buy a ticket to a show for the evening. He took the materials Nic passed across the table in a manila envelope. It could have been information on the terrorist cell or something for Marten's manuscript. He would head back upstairs to his room to take serious study in private.

14

YYZ

SPIRITS TURNED BITTER BY THE POISON OF ENVY.
ALWAYS ANGRY AND DISSATISFIED. EVEN THE LOST ONES.
THE FRIGHTENED AND MEAN ONES. EVEN THE ONES WITH
A DEVIL INSIDE. ALL THAT YOU CAN DO IS WISH THEM WELL.

—RUSH

After rising in the morning Marten did some quick reading to gather some information on the original Toronto 18 plot as that was a cell, he didn't recall much about, since the plot was foiled. His paper did indeed cover the story, but since the Canadian misfits didn't actually kill anyone, it quickly dissipated from the Detroit media; though it was a sensationalist story for some time in the Canadian press back then, as it could portend Canada as a major target going forward after the relative calm. If there were to be a resurgence of that plot, how much ink it might garner over the next week depends on the evidence that this plot is not just like all the other rumors.

The 2006 Toronto 18 offensive was clearly far more aspirational than operational, as the nomenclature came to be known. They had a lot of loose thoughts and not a whole lot of action. How long the authorities might let this current potential copy-cat situation "cook" to gather more evidence and insnare more potential conspirators was something Marten wanted Nic to address.

They had a bold vision, though. They seemed to aspire to a very multi-faceted approach: a blend of original and copycat tactics such as using IEDs to destroy landmarks and injure those in proximity. Their team consisted of two- or three-man crews, although several were more like boys, being under the age of eighteen. The other of the five or six teams would diverge with the other subgroups engaging in Mumbai India resorts assaults. They were going into the resorts but using semi-automatic rifles to shoot up random people who happened to be at the target locations. They would determine the location by driving around to find a place with a lot of traffic that day and then open fire upon the crowds. Others used their transport vehicles as a weapon and mow down pedestrians, as seen in many London outbreaks. Then they engaged in roving café-to-café-style incursions.

What most made that terror cell, as still officially referred, unique was having five young members. Certainly, we have known terrorists groom children to become future terrorists. To actually employ them in an assault, however, was different. Sure, children would be recruited and sent into battle to kill wearing murder-suicide vests, but that was usually reserved for warzones.

The Beltway sniper, John Allen Muhammad, began his shooting spree of terror once he had taken seventeen-year-old Lee Boyd Malvo under his wing. Most terrorists avoid using underage boys to avoid angering the public by including children in their heinous plans. Details of how the schemers were exposed was unclear. Certainly, intelligence agencies tried to keep such things secret as long as possible so as not to give away their undercover agents as doing so would risk other undercover operations. To protect "sources and methods" in the vernacular.

Would this potential news from Nic about potential Canadian copycats take as long to weed out Marten wondered?

Other Canada related events also came to mind. Originating in Canada, the millennium bomber's degree of nervousness gave him away at the Canadian and United States border. His plan to bomb the Los Angeles airport was thwarted after many trips back to his Algerian homeland to learn more about crude bomb making. He was stopped while crossing over into United States at Seattle and searched, revealing a large cache of explosives. Easily crossing provinces or state borders is one thing, but crossing international borders is another.

The Algerian born Ahmed Ressam was radicalized in Algeria. He was part of the Islamic Fundamentalist Party that actually managed to win election but was prevented from taking power by the Alger military, which caused a civil war in 1992. Many stayed to fight in their homeland to develop another fascist state. Others who were too cowardly to fight in a more official war between sides fled abroad going to relative peaceful grounds to contemplate lashing out with violence there.

As to the radicalization of Muhammed and the Toronto 18, that came out during their trials. Muhammed was born and raised and self-radicalized in the United States. Most of the Toronto 18, however, like Ressam, were born in various unstable nations and radicalized abroad. Why they hated Canada and Canadians was a mystery after having lived among the so very polite and welcoming society. Marten nervously chuckled about the politeness of Canadians as he recalled the ringleader of the Toronto 18 in court literally tried to apologize to the very people he was otherwise previously planning to try and murder. Zakaira Amara stated both that he felt his "terrorist plans were divinely aborted" and "I have no excuses or explanations. I deserve nothing than your complete and absolute contempt."

Neither the jury nor the judge seemed to accept his conciliary tone. He and the others were convicted. For Amara's role as mastermind, he received the harshest sentence in Canadian history under the Canadian Anti-Terrorism Act that passed Canadian Parliament after 9/11 and had as wide-sweeping powers as the Patriot Act in the United States.

Some groups may potentially resurrect the plan, which would be devasting. Or they may make other plans to spread mayhem and stretch the response operations, is the most diabolical and potentially lethal; aside from using planes as missiles into buildings. The public is likely left in the dark until the Royal Canadian Mounted Police and other agencies started raiding the hideouts of the conspirators. If Ontario officials raised their terror threat level or otherwise commented on credible threats, that could tip off the terrorists as to the efforts to catch them. If the public were alerted in advance, any and every cell in any state of planning for an assault would likely scatter. That could disrupt an immediate threat, or worse it could prompt a cell to move up their assault increasing carnage rather than trying to obstruct it.

Marten headed down for this other meetup at the Dig-site restaurant, settled into a booth, and awaited his friend's arrival. Hopefully some things might be cleared up. Perhaps Nic would have second thoughts on sharing much and instead focus on passing Marten other notes about other past attacks he knew Marten was considering for his book, though he likely shared all those in the manila folder Marten already possessed from him. Maybe it would be something he could write about in his book, but not something Nic would likely want to have Marten take back to his paper. Detroit papers often covered events having to do with US Citizens' friends up highway 101 - being one of Detroiters quick escape options. Toronto, for Detroiters, was like a world away in spirit, even though many thought of it as part of one big North American block in many respects; being outside the United States; but just next door. Marten would likely just stay silent, unless it came to the paper via other sources, for the obvious reasons that the wrong release of information too soon could exacerbate the situation and result in deaths if the authorities moving on the cell were upended.

The prematurely graying Nic slid into the booth across from Marten with a cheery hello and outstretched hand. Marten gripped it firmly and heartly gave it a shake. It was the formality that was dispensed from the day before. "It's been a long time before yesterday's meet up my friend," Nic said.

"It sure has," replied Marten.

The conversation stayed strangely generic and off topic from where it was expected to go. Marten had become uncharacteristically comfortable as Nic continued with the "let's catch up on our lives" conversation.

"Remember my ex'? She was that somewhat shy and very low self-esteemed thing. The one that claimed to have little interest in money but when we no longer had the time and money to devote to her desires, her interest disappeared! Even though we had both agreed that my taking the homeland security reassignment here in Nevada was a good thing. Guess she was only reminiscing about the good times we had here; but that, of course, were only our almost yearly visits."

Marten and Hope had only really met Debbie a few times and had had little more than idle conversations. Nic pointed to the time in 2003 that they were supposed to travel together to the southwestern rim of the Grand Canyon by car. When Hope and Marten informed them that they had already booked an event Debbie had refused to alter the plans by a day. They did venture to the Red Rock Canyon together, hopping in the usual Envoy Marten would have while in Nevada and following the Drive Yourself Tours Hope had purchased over the Internet on another joint vacation day they shared.

In retrospect, Nic recalled that they had come together only when it was on Debbie's terms. A boating trip to enjoy the hot summer of 2000 and a dinner engagement with two other couples that Marten and Nic both knew. Looking back, it was clear that Nic had turned a blind eye to his ex-wife's selfishness. Those seven years they lived as one were wonderful when Nic was doing what his wife wanted to do. He eventually recognized her self-centeredness more and more over time; driving a wedge between them.

He now noticed that she was a reluctant partner in their arrangement. He didn't care; his desire was only to remain true to his bride. She, however, viewed the relationship as having a husband in tow as opposed to it being a joint journey of two equals. No longer was she concerned with the "give" part of the "give and take" that is required in a healthy marriage. The demands of Nic's new employment move from Michigan to Nevada became a source of derision too.

Marten was well aware that Nic still loved only his ex-wife. What others might see as bitterness was just Nic's way of coping with his loneliness and desire to reunite with his wife; at least in theory. Deep down he knew that unless she had come to realize marriage requires compromise, a second go 'round would most certainly end in the same fate as the marriage. The years had been difficult on Nic.

The countless hours of psychological studies governmental training Nic had gone through in order to understand human nature didn't matter when it came to dealing with his own life. Self-examination, and those in one's immediate sphere, often a far different proposition. Nic wished his wife would return or that he could just somehow get her out of his head. If he could just convince himself to hate her, it might be possible to move on. But hating her could never happen. Just seeing Marten brought back a flood of memories of all the good times Nic shared with Debbie back in Michigan. Nic living in Vegas following their separation was different. While he thought of her on a daily basis, he was able to separate the two lives. But the tide of emotions would uncontrollably rush in given the right stimulus.

How she could erase all the good times and dwell only on their missteps in life was inconceivable to him. The occasional negative thought would enter his mind, but it would quickly subside he would never let them overshadow the good times he wouldn't trade for anything in the world – except for another chance now. How was it you give your entire heart and soul to one person only to have them leave you empty and cold?

None of that really mattered, but he just couldn't get the pain to go away and shake these ghosts from haunting him. He's just been existing of late, drifting through each day praying that he could somehow discover just what he could do to make things better. How will he begin to redeem himself?

Money isn't anything, but it is everything when it comes to surviving this life. You need money to buy the mansion on the hill in order to fulfill the storybook romance. The princess bride must have a kingdom to rule. Fifth, sixth, and so on, honeymoons don't materialize out of thin air. If money isn't the whole art gallery, it certainly was part of the picture. Times were good as long as the money flowed. Like too many couples, the more time they spent apart, the better and longer the relationship lasted. As long as he went off to war, so to speak, and brought home the bacon, the good times continued. Confusion and uncertainty seemed the only constant, an apparent consequence of a marriage where only one individual was willing to talk, willing to try, wishing to go on as one.

This, Nic believed, was yet another test here on earth. He was not going to allow the constricting notions pull him into the darkness and evil that consumes the hearts, minds, and souls, of all good peoples' enemies. He knew he must fight, as we all must, to keep love in his heart. The very darkness that reduces to ashes all traces of good that now drives our enemies must be resisted.

Marten saw Nic's face awash with the flood of emotion that he realized was flowing through his mind. While the moment passed fairly quickly, Marten still understood it was there. It was those painful emotions he was constantly trying to suppress along with the stress of his work that had begun to rapidly age Nic. Along with the sudden onset of gray entering into the mix of Nic's blonde mustache and beard. Crows-feet were becoming visible at the sides of his eyes. Lines across the forehead were becoming more prominent. Marten thought to himself, my friend must be under a whole lot of pressure and is visibly aging well beyond his actual years.

Marten wished he could assist his friend with the inner pain he felt but knew it was a private burden. The best friend that Marten could be, would be a friend that was available to listen when Nic needed a sympathetic ear. Other than that, he recognized that Nic needed just to elude that painful reality. A joke or two might help break Nic's funk, but nothing surfaced. The attentive friend would have to continue to just listen.

While some people were trying to shelter themselves from a painful reality, others were just plain alien to real hardships. Marten was well versed in dealing with so many jaded individuals who were somewhat shielded from the harshness of the tough side of life. Every big city had its well-to-do sections where people were getting by relatively comfortable but who were also downtrodden emotionally. There seemed to be such a large percentage of society that stumbled through life, oblivious to the darker side of living. So many are unwilling to fight so hard and give up so much to provide the freedoms enjoyed in our country. Blissful are the ignorant, those with more than enough to just coast through life that they do not see and feel compelled to care about their fellow man. While others bear the weight of the world on their shoulders, much as the United States has now been seemingly thrust into position of being the world's protectorate. Many resent having to be the world's policemen while others welcome the role as the bulwark against socialism, and a "force for good."

Two of Marten's favorite quotes were both from Ronald Reagan:

"Socialists ignore the side of man that is the spirit. They can provide you shelter, fill your belly, with bacon and beans, treat you when you are ill, all the things guaranteed to a prisoner or a slave. They don't understand that we also dream."

As well as: "If fascism ever comes to America, it will come in the name of liberalism."

Some rise to the challenges – both home and abroad – for the good of all. Others just reap all the benefits. Marten and Nic both fully believed that those who take on the added burden in this life build a family legacy and secure a better place in the hereafter. The irony is not lost in this latest test between good and evil here on earth. Nic knew Marten understands but verbalized anyway how the struggle is between those who wish to take life and those who work to preserve it and even better to secure the freedoms of others. Someone has to care! Someone must fight or those who blindly sit on the sidelines would fall prey to the darkness before ever knowing what hit them. Hiding one's head in the sand provides no real protection from the mounting threats of today's society – whether you are seeing them directly head-on barreling at you or not they can still bowl you over. We shall all be judged for our actions or inactions one day. Some choose to be sheep dogs, others just sheep; or worse an ostrich and easy pray for those higher up the food-chain, figurative or literal.

"The only thing required for evil to prevail is for good men to do nothing," said philosopher Edmund Burke. In the land of political correctness, it's a sin to use the word "men" and not "people." Language was different then, and it was meant as people as "men" represented a shortened version of "mankind," meaning all people, but do not try to explain any of that to a WOKE person. The Orwellian newspeak is all that matters now. Fascists want to define all the terms, control the language as a means of confusing and manipulating the opposition. Often to further divide and conquer, and as Orwell depicted in his *Animal Farm* book – the leftist elites would remain one of those treated more equal than others.

Many seek to destroy the way of life of everyone else to make up for their own inadequate sense of righteousness in their own lives, Nic continued to tell Marten. The few are fighting for the greater good of the masses that live in their shells. The "greater good" is yet another warped and twisted term to meet a Marxist or fascist agenda rather than deal in honest discussion, like with the idea of it taking a village to raise a child. That used to be a general idea of neighbor looking out for neighbor not that the government should usurp the role of the (conservative) parents as Hillary Clinton uses it.

Many though oblivious to both domestic and foreign politics were jolted to the harshness of reality on 9/11; now far too many have gone back to sleep, which is certainly one of Marten's motivations to write his book. None of the families that were ripped apart deserved the horror that entered their lives. The complacent met evil that day, and now so many suffer for it. Some who were not directly affected were also jolted into consciousness, only to go back to their own little worlds when the news coverage subsided.

For those who were truly enlightened, and those whose lives were inexplicably altered directly by the actions of those bent on criminal intent, they will never be able to go back to a lulled sense of security and peace of mind. Once the genie is out of the bottle, you can't put it back. Once you've seen the world for what it really was, a small divide between the good and the evil with the great expanse of humanity floating on auto pilot in the middle, it is difficult to turn back from the brink of that abyss.

Evil, it seems, never sleeps. It never takes vacations. It's always on the prowl for its next unaware, unenlightened, ill-informed sleepwalker looking to terrify and then hopefully gain control over as you can only be terrorized if you are unwilling to recognize the everyday threats. Incapable of dealing with the fact that evil must be confronted, it just won't co-exist if you pretend it won't affect you.

Criminals, as well as terrorists, fit general profiles. If all the crime scene investigation television programs had taught the general unwashed masses anything, it was that law enforcement agencies had always used profiling to build a list of potential suspects. Profiling is as important now as ever, Nic pointed out.

Disenfranchised individuals who had felt life was unfair and that they were uniquely owed something in return for the unfairness somehow think they were now better than everyone else and deserving a special place in history – special allowances, special privileges, not that of equal rights and equal opportunity the US Constitution afforded. Equal rights and equal opportunity are, Marten believed, for those willing to be peaceable, coexist and strive toward their own dreams rather than in envy and hate obsess over what other people have and how they might take it from them rather than work hard and earn if for oneself in a simple sense of sound religious tenants versus socialist tenants. Others above even that, that they are imbued to be masters and rulers of all, and others their slaves. Only they were exclusively qualified to usher in this new age of enlightenment, and it would come only through the death of others, innocent men, women, and children.

Somehow, they had come to view themselves as chosen to be forgiven, honored even, for acts of the most horrendous affront to decency and goodness. Somehow, they thought they could accost the very laws of God, in the name of God, and yet obtain reward for such acts. It indeed takes a uniquely warped individual to allow for such backward thinking, that they would receive a special reward in the afterlife. In the mind of the average person, they'd be right, but it wouldn't be ascension they would be receiving.

You'll probably find those fitting the terrorist profile at the Hooters Casino and Hotel trying to hit on the Hooters girls, Nic thought. These Islamists, that would like to portray themselves as so very devout, are a real joke. Sadly, too, are the hypocrite class in America, the self-loathers who profess one thing while acting otherwise. There are the power-hungry elites who try to soak up as much money they can get their hands on – especially if they can steal it by any means necessary – pretend they care so much about females while degrading them with their hedonistic pursuits they claim to hate.

Want to find a terrorist, find a local strip club. That's where they'll be, looking at as much female skin as they can while they've got their supposed girlfriend or wife wrapped up behind at least a veil or headscarf, and potentially beyond that a hijab, niqab, or burka.

Yes, it is indeed true even the Christian Bible calls for modest dress among faithful women. To what degree that means may change over time. Modest dress means different things when in public versus gatherings among friends, and it means something different between Christian denominations let alone by way of comparison of and within or amongst Islamic sects.

In reality, Nic believed, no one should look to traditional Islamic practices when it comes to the virtue and purity of women. Young Muslim men can be the biggest hypocrites you'll ever find on the planet when it comes to the treatment of women. Dressing and acting one way in one environment or locale and being completely opposite in another. When pressed, he offers that of Muslim tourists shunning their traditional clothing for more lax and western considered norms of modesty when traveling from the Middle East to western nations. Even the definition was very different in Iran under the Shah and that nation being more in tune with western norms prior to the Islamic revolution and rise of the Ayatollahs.

The fact that they can live such a life of lies, double standards, and two-faced hypocrisy was beyond Nic, that is until he started dealing with the GIJIAS scum on a daily basis. It really comes down to jealousy, not hatred. They want the American way of life. They'll act out the lifestyle they claim to detest, then perform an about face and try to blow up as many innocent women and children as they can in one blast.

Marten listened attentively. He knew Nic would certainly never blanketly stereotype all Muslims nor all Arabs, and they both clearly understood the distinctions of not all terrorists being Arab or even Muslim. He had never shown any racial tendencies in the couple of decades plus years that they had known each other. Their very candid, as it had been for many of those years, relationship allowed them to become well acquainted with each other's concerns, feelings, and deepest secrets; it's what made their friendship and working relationship coexist in total harmony and trust.

Nic was such a part of Marten's life, while they all resided in Michigan, that Nic was Martens youngest daughter's godfather, and remained a close friend even after Nic had moved from Michigan for the Nevada assignment.

As they chit-chatted, Marten's mind briefly drifted, and he thought it had to be difficult to deal with terrorists every day and yet also have to acquire adequate evidence to obtain the legal precedent to pursue them. It must be maddening to have to allow these loose cannons wander about American (as well as all other Western, as they still have some semblance of being, free nations') streets while trying to intercept additional intelligence and delicately attempt to corner these would be assassins prior to actually committing their terrorist plots, so they can put the scum behind bars forever.

Even standard criminal class lowlifes are free to speak of potential actions; not until an actual movement to engage is made can the criminal be arrested. Racketeering (RICO) laws apply in some cases and allow for the arrest of criminals plotting, but without being caught in the act, it's much harder to get a conviction in court.

While all threats had to be taken seriously, they also have to be viewed for their national or potential international impact. Actual threats to the whole of Vegas or Laughlin itself were deemed less likely, as he figured the terrorist really wouldn't want to destroy this haven of hedonism they so vehemently rallied against, but so readily personally embraced. "Letting our guard down to the possibilities that an attack might be carried out in this region," Nic explained, "would certainly welcome an attack, as these targets might then take on an added luster if believed easier to strike."

When the bill came, Marten had further evidence that Nevada's tourism had been transformed from pre-9/11 days based upon the price-tag for their simple breakfast. Marten used to love to head up to the Holiday Inn that used to exist on the Vegas Strip for $1.99 morning deal. The inexpensive steak-and-lobster deal used to be a staple at the Stardust, long torn down. Late night steak and eggs at Maxim. Breakfast, which one could still purchase across America for just a few dollars was now a $15 tab. Beef was also not half the cost of anywhere else in the US anymore. When you wanted steak, you used to be able to dine on steaks with a hamburger budget. Not anymore. Now, if you want steak, you pay for steak, more a caviar budget!

Suddenly Nic leaned in, and Marten knew the tone of this meeting would likely finally get on-track as to where he expected it to be. Nic quietly went on to inform him that the intel he passed Marten yesterday was now proving to be stale and outdated. Nic conversed last night with additional contacts. There was a lot of confusion, attempts to deflect blame between agencies up around Toronto and even Ottawa. It seemed the cell had vanished, Nic told him. Now they were in the wind, Nic used the vernacular, and were thought to have used fake passports to venture to either Afghanistan or Syria. Was this to help garner foreign resources to obtain materials or were they abandoning the plot. Toronto unknowing, and unable to reacquire them for surveillance yet was an embarrassment.

Even just this hint proved the adage that an attack, even rumors of, could reverberate and potentially effect lives. Marten loved flying into the Toronto airport designated YYZ and catch a show in the

Theater District there. Now, however, Marten might still consider going while this unannounced sense of heightened alert existed but he would not consider taking his family over there for a visit anytime soon. Even Marten, who vocalized, we cannot allow terrorists to win, in this case was allowing it to affect him.

"The plot thickens," Marten casually let the thought pass through his lips. "Sorry, I do not mean to make light, but you know I'm in author mode right now!"

Nic just chuckled and replied, "Yes, no laughing matter but we have to try and keep a bit of a lighter nature and even use our sense of humor at times, or we'll go crazy."

Nic proceeded to then lighten the mood further interjecting, "A guy goes into a bar, and says: 'Hey bartender. Give me a Coke with a Viagra.' To which the bartender looks at him funny. The man then adds, What? I need a really stiff drink!"

Nic had thought of that joke long ago and loved to tell it. While it was obvious where it was going, they still both wondered why no professional comedian told it, although, they had heard variations on the joke over the years. They had previously chuckled over the contemplation whether someone overheard Nic telling it one of his million times and stole it, or at least the basic premise to then try to slyly craft a variation. Well, in other words, not stole, perhaps maybe subconsciously 'inspired' the similar lines of jokes being heard now.

Marten provided a brief polite chuckle and responded, "I can see you still haven't found a *good* sense of humor!" Not wanting to pass the chance to get a good-hearted dig in on his friend, he continued, "You know you set yourself up for that, right?"

Nic nodded "Yes, yes, yes, and so far as my bad puns go, as you know, will always remain a certainty." Nic then went on to tell another one of his original, but not very funny, jokes. "Is it TO BE or NOT TO BE, that is indeed the question. Because if it is 2 B then I have BINGO!"

Marten stood and announced, "and with that, I think we're done here." He reached out his hand. Nic outstretched his. They gave a hearty handshake. Then they were on their separate ways again. Marten made a quick escape from the table, leaving Nic to cover the cost of the breakfast.

As Marten walked away, he chuckled again. Perhaps he could include some of those jokes in his book to preserve them for Nic. With things today always being so damn serious, he just now made the final decision that some amount of humor must be included. If you do not laugh, you will be crying all the time. He chuckled at his own lame comedic pondering.

Next on the itinerary, of course, would be the next casino over where he knew the Laugh-a-Minute Comedy Club would likely have seats open for a show. He laughed out loud again, much to the likely bemusement of those around him as he passed along the open-air gaming floor of the Pyramid on his way back toward the elevators. Here I look like a crazy person now just wandering along laughing for no apparent reason it would appear to others, he thought. He was laughing, this time, call-back fashion, in comedy vernacular, to the notion of whether or not the particular comedian Marten will land up seeing would be in the 'he stole the Viagra variation joke from Nic, line of thinking.

Perhaps they may have a magician intermingled in the acts? Marten wondered. Hopefully a decent one unlike last time when the magician was so bad, he made the audience disappear, vanishing, practically running, out of the exits.

Nearing the elevator, Marten thought he'd drop a few coins and try his luck. Dropping a few coins, however, was a thing of the past, except for the specialty establishment on Freemont Street in downtown Vegas proper. Casinos long gave way to bill accepters and all digital recording of winnings and losses. They kept the familiar ding-ding-ding to keep the gambler excited and hopefully engaged longer – even though the house was winning ninety-nine percent of the time.

When done with a 'one-arm-bandit' and hitting the 'payout' button was far less exciting too now. Again, the machine would ding-ding-ding, but zero coins would drop, instead a boring piece of paper would be produced with your 'cash value' on it to move to the next machine with or to the cashier to obtain the real cash value.

Marten put in his money and pulled the handle but no luck. He tried again, resulting in another nothing outcome spin. At least these were physical and tangible machinery, but indeed all computer-generated results and tabulations calculating spin odds then one of several preprogrammed video display results to provide visual to user of the premeditated outcome. Marten wondered how or why anyone would trust the now plentiful online gaming options, or apps that let you play right in the palm of one's hand via their smartphone. But, in the end, they are all just computer driven now – even these with spinning wheels and flashing lights. Legit apps from Nevada firms; or even the Michigan casinos might release as a brand, being affiliated with casino chains; would still be subject to the strict, still in favor of the gaming providers, laws and regulations of States allowing gaming, but not a complete scam with no real odds of winning ever some other off-shore, wild-wild-west and unregulated offerings could be.

Marten's mind snapped-back to the new Toronto plotters. What too then might come of other previously identified plots on United States' targets. The Brooklyn Bridge, the Ambassador Bridge between Detroit and Windsor, US government buildings, LAX, key internet hubs to disrupt Internet traffic so many now have as an everyday part, no longer considered a luxury; Three Mile Island one of a few nuclear power plants, "Fermi II" nuclear plant, located in Detroit southern suburbs.

The list goes on and on – United Nations building being another prime NYC location, Disney World Florida which was the stated primary target of who later became the Pulse Nightclub shooter, a flag manufacturer in the US as preeminent producer of "free nations'" flags, key heavy-vehicle makers in order to attempt to disrupt farming and general construction across North America, Saudi Arabia's embassy in Washington DC.

Simple Duck-duck-go or GIBIRU engine searches easily confirm many. Much information of previously identified and at times foiled plots, can be found. Today would-be terror cells could just find an outline for their misdeeds online. Detroit, as all also known as "The Motor City" a long list of targets, including some aimed at one or more of "The Big 3" auto producers.

On the long list of other target options includes infrastructure, various landmarks like the Arch, as well as the Pyramid in Nevada.

How many of these marks for prior attacks that were abandoned might be resurrected also?

15

ATROCITY

MY PEOPLE ARE DESTROYED FOR A LACK OF KNOWLEDGE.

—Hosea 4:6

*H*itler and Stalin caused the death of over one hundred million Jews, and not necessarily only during the German and Russian empires of the 1930s and 1940s. What about their roles, and does it lead to belittling the overall degree of the atrocities and the roles of society as a whole?

What is the Islamic fundamentalists death-toll to date? What might it escalate to? These are ever-changing estimates. The Islamist-inspired killings need to be included in the toll. But what of the deaths being racked up behind the virtual walls of China against the Uyghur Muslim population?

The Communist Chinese Party has not allowed any information about terrorist attacks on Chinese soil to escape beyond its iron-grip on the nation's media and Internet. Nonetheless, they insist that enslaving the Uyghurs is necessary for the preservation of the communist state and necessary response to GIJIA terrorism. Communists and fascists always need a scapegoat to justify their genocides and keep others under their thumbs, pliable, in-line, for fear of being targeted next.

The Holocaust Museum in Houston, Texas, well documents the genocide in Bosnia. The ethnic and religiously diverse populace lived in somewhat harmony under the control of the iron-fisted Communists of Yugoslavia. However, that all ended when factions longed for their own states. As communism began to fall when Reagan won the Cold War, though seeming later resurgence as the West tried to focus on a peace dividend over vigilance, in the 1990s, Croatia and Slovenia declared themselves as sovereign republics.

Serbia invaded Croatia and Slovenia under the guise of protecting the Christian populations living within Bosnia. An ethnic purge then began. The horrors of concentration and death camps the world thought died with the conclusion of the Second World War dotted the map within the former Yugoslav borders. The United Nations Security Council voted on military action, and member nations under the blue helmets rolled in eventually to end the conflict. Before the UN could get there and countless thousands were ritually slaughtered and an estimated twenty-three thousand women, children, others of fighting age were relocated to Muslim territories. Whether it was genocidal slaughter or not is still disputed.

There has been a history of Muslims fighting Muslims though also. Consider how Saddam, the Iraqi dictator, and a Sunni Muslim, took on the Kurds in the north. Shia Iran and Sunni Iraq officially warred for eight years – many more unofficially – until Iran accepted a United Nations cease-fire resolution. That didn't stop them, however, to continue to cleanse Sunni's within their borders. Iran has continued to fund proxy, subversive forces within other nations to kill Christian, Jew, and Muslim, alike.

The death tolls of these Muslim conflicts to this day remain disputed. People were rounded up, hauled off, and buried in mass graves across many nations. Historians believe the number has a floor of one million or a ceiling of over two million. That is a lot of unaccounted for people, presumed dead.

It should surprise no one, however, that the slaughter would ignite again at some point after the conclusion of the Second World War when poorly drawn lines creating new nations across the Middle East were established, especially in the minds of many that each of the Muslim sects should have had their own nation states. The same debate raged again post Second Gulf War and whether Iraq should have been broken into three – for each of the differing Muslim sects. Others argue it would never make a difference. As there would always be some ambitions toward genocide of others, and not surprising the current aggression in the Middle East, given that Iran means "the Land of Aryans" which should ring a familiar 1930s Germany refrain as to also understanding their sense of superiority.

Marten's thoughts kept leaping between the distant past, recent past, the here and now, and what it portends for the future.

Hitler himself, as well as other NSDAP representatives, had visited several lands throughout the region to meet with many established leaders and even several of the up-and-comers who would later be the players shaping continued conflict to last many more decades and on into the next century. There was much collaboration among the German leadership and Arab leadership throughout the

Second World War. That the Arabs would then go on to emulate the NSDAP should not be a shock to anyone, considering they both have a lust for bloodshed. The militaristic side of the Islamic fundamentalists sects even back then admired and were eager to join forces with Hitler and his operations in their regions. Therefore, after brief peace as Europe rebuilt, the destruction resumed as those wannabe Hitler types consolidated power and looked to expand and engage in their own hideous dreams to cleanse the earth of whom they hate.

As the saying goes: "those who fail to learn from history are condemned to repeat it." The more accepted terminology now: "history may not exactly repeat, but it sure does rhyme an awful lot."

Marten wasn't sure how much of this he needed to cover in *Terrorist Tracks* as there were countless books already well documenting these wars. Although many allowed modern Islamic fundamentalists to rewrite the history as they'd preferred. No wonder how easily a Neville Chamberlain mindset could once again reemerge today, with so little understanding of historical precedence.

For many across the sand regions, the rise of power of Adolf Hitler and the Nazi party became the great Islamic hope in the Middle East that viewed the British empire at the time as peacekeepers and in control of the area as an occupying force. Germany was viewed as the only power that would be able to free the supposed oppressed Muslim culture, but really was just constraints on the GIJIAS and not the Islamic faithful masses, from the British. To this end, the Baath party (yes, that Baath party, of Saddam Hussein) in Syria and Iraq, as well as open relation between the Iranian Shah, worked in concert with the Nazi party to provide resistance throughout the Middle East during the years of the Second World War.

Marten's meditations again wandered between his grandparent's era, his parent's age, and that of his children.

Early Middle East terrorist groups, such as the Muslim Brotherhood, officially based in Egypt, formed to free itself of the supposed Western oppression. Hitler's Germany was to be its saving grace. Others then formed to join the jihad, or struggle. This marked the beginning of what seemed an unofficial quadripartite pact between Hamas, Islamic Jihad, Hezbollah, and the Mujahadin, all forming independently at separate times but retaining close ties to the nation-states that aided in their growth by other various official governments in the Middle East so as to have unofficial proxy armies in other region states.

The monarch governments, such as King Farouk's, were put in place throughout the Middle East and southwest Asia by the British and French. They were loosely veiled as Western puppet regimes. Many, especially radicals that lusted for their own power, in the region longed for a bit more autonomy. They thought they may get it under Hitler, if they aided Germany to defeat the British and the French. Western allies after the war were eager to end conflict by granting many of these same murdering thugs to have their own land. Britain was eager to withdraw and leave them to their own devices. It was short sighted, and they should not have been so easily convinced they would remain happy fighting among themselves.

Iran, known as Persia until after the Second World War, is an Islamic Republic but not an Arab state. Though declared as an "Islamic Republic," but instead really a Persian state. This, in part, is what helped fuel the fire of battle between Iran and Iraq; until that ended and their alliance and allegiance to destroy Israel and its Western allies took to the fore for a while.

Following the Second World War the United States and Iran became allies as the United States helped rebuild Iran and train its forces, foolishly believing they could get them out of the fascistic mindset, which seemed to be working for a short time. America was even providing nuclear technology to Iran at that time. But that alliance eroded during the Carter administration and the Islamic revolution deposed the Shah. Then Iran barely survived the Iraqi attack as they relied on decades-old technology. It was the best the West was willing to provide.

The US and Iran alliance ended in the mid-1970s. That's about when Iran started calling the US the Great Satan and when the Ayatollah Khomeini, an extremist militant Muslim, came to power. This culminated in the Iran hostage crisis in 1979 during the Jimmy Carter presidency, which cemented Iran's leadership's hatred of the West.

Some in the West still hold out hope that an eventual counter-revolution can and will happen. During the Obama presidency the seeds started to bloom, which demonstrated that the peoples and their Islamic fundamentalist leaders are divergent, in what became known as the Green Revolution. With zero support, let alone any behind the scenes aid, it was quickly trampled. The underpinnings remain should Western alliances actually attempt to overthrow the Islamic regime and return Iran back to a more secular state like existed under the Shah.

The conflict with Iran served to temporarily shift American allegiance to Iraq in order to balance the power against the new

Iranian push to establish a greater Persian empire, a stated goal of the regime under Khomeini. Iran pushed the West directly into the conflict by closing the Persian Gulf shipping lanes and striking at a US naval vessel. These hostilities led to the underlying uneasy state of Cold War among the formerly warring states. That is, until after Obama withdrew all forces following the Second Gulf War, and the US invasion of Iraq toppled Saddam. Subsequent regimes in Iraq have had more progress with Iran. The West, however, wanted them to remain perpetual enemies, to maintain a sense of balance in the region and keep in check the influence of ISIS, which were aroused due to the vacuum Obama's troops withdrawal and Iraqi Army incompetence caused.

Marten's mind raced, again. He thought of the far past, near past, present, and future. His thoughts were colliding. Back and forth different points of view battled in his brain. How would he sort it all out to offer to his readers? How much needed to be included? How much would his reader take upon their own, to read other books for more information on the subject? He couldn't expound everything or his book would be *War and Peace* length, and modern attention spans could not endure such effort.

Following the Second World War, Middle East governments sought dictatorial control in the Nazi model. Saddam Hussein's rise to power followed in Hitler's footsteps. Saddam, like Hitler, was a low-level soldier and petty political operative before being catapulted to the top of their movements and cast into power. Saddam even adopted the Nazi salute and goose-step style march for his forces. Further, he adopted personally loyal troops – the Republican guard – styled after the Nazi SS. They were the elites who were to be even more dedicated and loyal to the head of state than the national army.

In the 1940s, terrorist groups like the Muslim Brotherhood took up arms against the newly formed Israeli state and nations that supported it. Again, their hatred drove them to scapegoat the Jewish populations as an excuse to conspire and war against external rather than internal conflicts. Providing its peoples an enemy helped keep their homelands, for a time, a bit more stable. The divided Muslim sects, however, would keep flaring in bouts over the decades. Tension, animosity, and further polarization took place following the Israeli and Egyptian peace summits. They viewed government states throughout the Middle East as selling out to Western influence and pressure. The results were assassinations of many peace-seeking leaders such as, Nassar, Anwar Sadat, Menachem Begin, and more. The Egyptian leadership under Nassar cracked down on the Muslim Brotherhood, which pushed the organization, and others like it, underground and into as many nations across the Middle East as they could take up occupancy; other fundamentalist leaders were happy to oblige and openly welcome them as they looked to bolster their own power, control, and influence.

One of the Islamic fundamentalist writings of the time around 1964 was *Milestones of the Road*. Several of those authors went on to lead the new terrorist movements, including terrorist plots to destroy targets along the Nile River. They laid the groundwork for today's modern martyr mentality.

Egyptian Islamic Jihad formed from the split of the elder leadership of the Islamic Brotherhood and the younger members desiring to escalate, terrorist attacks. Most of those arrested and tried for Sadat's assassination were members of the Egyptian Islamic Jihad. Some members that were later released, such as Ayman al Zawahiri, known as the father of the murder-suicide bomber, became founding members of al Qaeda.

The West even funded and supplied these organizations to fight the Soviets during the Cold War in such places as Afghanistan and elsewhere, which created the beasts we still fight today – despite the Biden administration abandoning our base there and leaving many trapped behind enemy lines. The Central Intelligence Agency, with the cooperation of the Pakistan government tried to create a puppet government within Afghanistan. It failed! The Taliban resurges.

Again, Marten's thoughts kept leaping between the distant past, recent past, and the here and now.

The invasion of Afghanistan by the Soviets led to yet more unstable alliances. The Soviets were trying to fight a proxy war with the US – as Putin again shows Russian aggression and expansionism, more proxy wars start over again today. It fell apart following the 1989 Soviet withdrawal from Afghanistan. After that, Western forces once again took their eye off the ball in the face of peace. They abandoned the likes of the Northern Alliance only to then have to beg for their help to fight on our behalf post 9/11. That shortsightedness allowed for Afghanistan to fester and the roots of 9/11 to arise. Marten thought this was clearly being repeated today.

Today, in the United States, the Islamic Brotherhood is not listed as a terrorist organization within its borders as it has publicly claimed to have denounced terrorism and now advocates for change via peaceful means, even though it had been identified as having violent wings in the Middle East and self-professed members, such as al Jawari, openly call for attacks against the US and its Western allies. Many see their public stance as only a façade.

The goal posts are always moving though. While the United States had at one point met the stated goal of Usama bin Laden to remove all forces from Saudi Arabian soil; if for only awhile. Whether it was intended to try and stop escalation of attacks by an act of appeasement, it failed. The terrorists continued their fight, showing their real motives of continuing terrorist attacks against the West for the sake of their enduring power.

Following 9/11, the United States joined up with its NATO allies, even though some of their motives were suspect. Governments underwent the overthrow of the Taliban in Afghanistan in order to destroy terrorist bases, with the most notorious being controlled by al Qaeda, which means "the Base," though as we all know now Pakistan was harboring both al Qaeda and the Taliban. Upon US withdrawal forces quickly reconstituted and retook the shaky nation. The years spent nation building and helping them become allies in the mold of West Germany and Japan after the Second World War, was now all for naught.

The Bunker Buster bombs used to attack the Tora Bora caves, built with the assistance of the CIA, were actually developed and used during the Second World War. We hoped to destroy al Qaeda from the air but experienced our first failure in the Afghanistan War. Decades before, in the European theatre, the Earthquake Makers were dropped as a means to strike hardened targets in Germany that were built during peace time with the desire to create a war-proof infrastructure.

Could such zealotry, hatred, and prejudice open the door for fanaticism and destruction on a large scale? That question was answered on 9/11. Whether it be in the name of a nationalist fervor or in the form of a religious purification, this was a new crusade. This time it was in the name of fundamentalist Islam. Usama bin Laden was not the president of a foreign country that could be defeated; though it was clear we had to go to war against the nation that harbored him. What of the nations that tacitly, if not overtly, supported such goals of destruction of the worlds' democratic nations?

Admission time. The United States' hands were not clean regarding immoral misdeeds. Marten's book when dealing with our own nation and its history would be an honest one.

What about FDR's war crimes? Millions of Japanese were huddled into concentration camps, though were not put to death, across the United States. These were United States citizens of Japanese descent but were Americans nonetheless.

German Americans, for the most part, did not suffer the same indignity. Nor had Russian Americans, even those who may have been a threat during the Cold War years. Joseph McCarthy didn't lock anyone away and has been proven right about the infiltration of Marxists, who have shown their ugliness. It's too bad the country only slowly reacted with disdain against the attack on freedom and justice that all were equal under the law and that individuals were free to choose their political affiliations, even if in line with those of a current world military adversary. Why does the winning of a war allow such inhumanity to go unrecognized and unpunished?

Marten again recalled the motion picture *The Siege* that portrayed concentration camps in America, this time to house Arabic descendants – or even worse, the wholesale degradation of a religion in the name of national security. Dearborn and the Bronx had high concentration of Arabs. Would they become targets? That answer, of course, is no, at least not so far.

What of Guantanamo Bay Cuba and the military prisons? Prisoners of the War on Terror and enemies posing a direct threat to the safety and security of countless innocent American citizens, as well as countless more foreign nationals either just visiting or currently residing in western democratic nations, are at stake. After all, just a small number of people are being held and not indiscriminately like was done during the Second World War.

Franklin Roosevelt was not the only blight on what America otherwise holds as purveyor of moral actions. Sadly too, going way back into America's past, many just forgive and prefer to allow be forgotten several indiscretions of Abraham Lincoln. During America's Civil War much was overlooked in the name of the necessity of Lincoln's abolitionist Republican Party to free the slaves as part of the preservation of the Union at all costs. That was another rabbit hole of history many hadn't ever learned or had forgotten. A brief mention, hopefully, would spur his readers to seek the myriad of books on those topics. Unfortunately, instead of reading and learning and putting things in historical perspective, many across the nation were in the name of clueless WOKEism demanding statues that helped provide historical perspective be torn down. So many were easily misled into violence and destruction in the name of WOKEism but really were only about keeping them obedient to the party of identity politics today.

There was the whole Andrew Jackson stain on America's past too. This rabbit hole, though, would be a distraction. Marten indeed wanted to acknowledge one can make mistakes but still maintain an overall claim of morality for the most part. As a Christian, he knew we are all frail and flawed humans needing God's grace. Past mistakes cannot disqualify, in whole, overall, many recent decades of change towards the better.

Marten's disdain toward those acting cruelly was aimed at not just those who were abusive or cruel toward fellow mankind but toward animals too. He believed that those who would disregard the well-being of animals would be open to allowing the degradation of humans, which could lead to the next holocaust. Those clearly willing to consider killing animals, or even slaughtering the unborn in the womb, were on a potentially even greater evil path. Marten viewed his pets as his family, loved and protected as any child would be.

These thoughts were a bit of an aside, but an important distinction to be broached. To what limitations does immorality hold itself, he thought, if often only temporarily pretends to hold a boundary. Excuses then creep in to allow additional immoral allowances and more killing.

In the end, atrocities of small scale always could easily advance to greater ones. Atrocities of the past, seemingly forgotten or from which lessons were never learned, still go on today right under their noses (some hidden, some in the open as with Russian onslaught of civilian targets in Ukraine). People prefer their delusion of security and that they would always be safe no matter how unhinged portions of the world might become around them.

16

MISDIRECTION

FAITH SHOULD NOT STAND IN THE WISDOM OF MEN,
BUT IN THE POWER OF GOD.

—1 Corinthians 2:5

*M*arten paused and contemplated, "There, but for the grace of God, go I." That sentiment was applicable to so many situations in life. There are people out there spreading confusion intentionally to discredit any and all faiths. He was firm in his belief.

Truth be told it is not just the GIJIAS that spread such misgivings and strife amongst all peoples. Much information, of religious nature, has been lost over time and more hidden or censored by being withheld from the masses. Each faith, and what only makes sense to each religious conviction, is to pass on only the knowledge and wisdom that is desired to be bestowed upon its believers.

Humankind has only been able to grasp a certain degree of enlightenment, in regard to its own pretexts, let alone 'supposedly' conflicting creeds. The very nature of the separation of many denominations of the Christian faith demonstrates that fact. Some of the very foundations of the Christian faith beg question. It is demanded that 'faith' allow acceptance, and that all truth shall be imparted upon our ascension. One can only pray they are right, and all our questions be answered in heaven.

It's hard to know what is true and what is made up by someone with an agenda. Ancient texts are incomplete and sometimes vague. Through various interpretations and translations, religions end up with different understandings of the tenants of their faith and thus we have different sects and denominations. In the end, the religious leaders just say you have to have faith and will understand in the hereafter.

The Roman emperor Constantine, when he became a Christian, sought to canonize the Christian Bible. He took the agreed-upon Old Testament books and gathered the writings and letters from the disciples and apostles to comprise the New Testament. It was still many years later later until the canon was formalized, and the debates will rage ad infimum about what was included and what was excluded properly or not.

The confusion and mistrust of religions, even of denominations or sects within one faith, is fueled by the existence of many versions and interpretations of the religious texts that exist. Christians have many translations of the Bible and many denominations. Likewise, multiple versions of Islamic texts and various interpretations of the Quran and Hadiths exist.

Certain Gnostic, from the Greek word *gnosis* (meaning "knowledge"), texts were withheld from the official Christian canon.

Other ancient text, such as identified by the Dead Sea scrolls, including the book of Jubilees, and other related religious texts were also dismissed. Some were considered outright fraudulent texts. Others were somewhat conflicting or texts that might cloud and confuse the overall messages.

Few realize that the Islamic Quran texts discuss Jesus directly. The Quran speaks more in depth of the nature of Mary and the virgin birth than the Christian Bible itself. Those who wish to divide dwell on the point that Muslim's view Jesus as a prophet, but not a Saviour. Yet many theologians contend Muslim's, Christians, and even the ancient Egyptians, worship the same God, and part of their contentions being Allah was first used in Aramaic and retained in Islam. The Quran retains the Genesis origin, Moses as a prophet, and other aspects. Though still others contend that Muhammed just attempted to create a "me too" religion for his Arab region sensibilities and used the tie-ins to build credibility for the later and great divergences of the texts and faiths.

While the Egyptians worshiped more than one god, the sub gods could be considered by many Christians as angels. Egyptian portrayal of ascension and return to the 'Valley of the Reeds,' or arguably, the Garden of Eden lend credence to such claims, in the minds of some. That being yet another rabbit hole Marten was choosing to avoid going down. Many other resources exist should anyone wish to further examine. Many texts refer to many of the same commandments as outlined as provided to Moses, the prophet who led the Jews in the Exodus from Egypt some three thousand plus years ago.

Ancient Egyptian texts portray a very similar virgin birth story many centuries before the time of Joseph and Mary. In the legend,

Horus was of a virgin birth by Osiris, who gave birth to Herod. The similarity in imagery is eerily analogous. That, however, is just one of many theories from Egyptian lore in dispute. Some argue Christians co-opted previous other religious precepts, as again Marten thought some contend about Muhammed, and adopted them as part of their own. These, again, will remain open questions that only the Creator can answer.

While the Quran discusses the youth of Jesus, the gospel of Thomas, which was omitted from Christian Bible, talks about the adolescence of Jesus Christ. Maybe the Christian leaders at the time did not trust that their followers would be able to comprehend Jesus' divinity if they were to gain insight into his youth. Maybe they thought if the followers thought of him as too much of a man, than talks God made flesh, they wouldn't believe he suffered, died, was buried, and raised again to save all mankind. That somehow to examine Jesus' humanity would somehow detract from, cause some that could potentially otherwise be brought into the flock would be hung up on and hinder one's ability to accept the notion of Jesus as Saviour.

Various religious texts, containing similar themes. Quran 5:32, for instance says that "whosoever kills a human being without [any reason like] manslaughter, or corruption on earth, it is as though he had killed all mankind. And whoever saves a life is it as thought he had saved the lives of all mankind." This commandment is consistent with the Holy Bible, old and new Testaments of the Jewish and Christian faiths. Yet, it would seem, that few Muslims speak out against the intolerance of the GIJIAS, who, in the name of their faith, attempt to lead all of Islam into all-out warfare against Christians and Jews, the people of the book (ahl al-kitāb), across the globe. The similarities are downplayed; the differences are embellished.

Even today, while we have come two millennium from Christ's birth, many people today cannot entertain any questions of their faith even if the additional information may further embolden it. People have only the most fundamental understanding of the faith they consider so much a cornerstone of their character. So many are unable or unwilling to educate themselves beyond their basic understanding. Many only cling to certain lines from their favored and deemed sacred book they'd memorized, sometimes even devoid of context needed for proper perspective and application. Marten thought about those who twist Jesus' words, distort the context, just as others; for own agenda not that of their faith; contort other supposed holy writs.

Sadly, Marten understood it was a part of everyday life for many, especially those looking to serve themselves for political gain, power, and control; they even bend Children's stories. Robin Hood no longer is a moral tale about returning that which was confiscated by the sheriff on behalf of the king. Instead, it has become a Marxist tale of redistribution. Stealing from the rich and giving to the poor. It is telling that they use the word *stealing, no matter the justification,* as a way to describe a moral story of their political ideology. Like with the twisting of the *Robin Hood* story, rather than the original taking back from the Sheriff, representative of a political state, and returning to whom it was confiscated.

Are these idle minds as equally idle in their hearts? Is professing one's beliefs enough? For those truly trying to actively participate, are they actually practicing what they are preaching? Many seem to just be going through the motions by attending church or going through the mechanics of the Islamic call to prayer, but are they really heeding the message of their God?

The issue is not one of questioning one's faith but rather questioning whether one is following the basic tenets of the creed or not, objectively speaking. Challenging devotion is different from questioning beliefs. Many seem afraid that if they test their own conviction by seeking knowledge of their faith beyond their preprogrammed accepted wisdom of their dedication, to back up or embolden their beliefs, will somehow endanger their salvation.

It is that abject fear that keeps them away from the religious texts that are claimed to be the very foundation of the commitment. Ephesians aside, many still hold it is that very salvation, however, may hinge on their willingness to understand and take actions within their faith, as well as their willingness and ability to follow within their particular faith. People, at times, pick and choose, as Islamists do with the Quran, other lines from their sacred texts book oft ignore other passages that provide additional context.

What of the countless Amish settlers in this country? While most do not consider the Amish ways of life in religious terms, it is indeed just that. They believe that a simple way of life, being closer to the environment to sustain their needs and way of life, brings them closer to God. Again, the same God, but different perspectives on maintaining the relation between the faithful and their God. American Amish, in some ways, similar to the notions put forth by GIJIAS of a more bygone era way of living – though they do not wish to kill those who do not believe the same.

Once again, one thought led to another as Marten contemplated all the faiths and religions and sects within, which were not all congruent, nor even necessarily logically connected. Studies show, children leave the nest of their upbringing faith and into more secular pursuits when they leave the family unit nest. Until such time children only seem to dutifully follow in the footsteps of their parents' religion, without any voluntary actions to study the faith they are embracing. They claim to believe, but cannot defend the faith, and why they can be so easily swayed when out of the family's embrace. It is that lack of understanding and knowledge that leads to abuse. Those with a command of the religious texts are free to wield their knowledge to mold or shape the unacquainted, those who do not really know and are susceptible to warping, with complete misinformation or even slight manipulations.

The misdirection of enthusiastic but naive individuals is what has seemingly led to the perverse acts of destruction, in which they target innocent people in the name of religion. It is only the uninformed mind, or those who are easily misled, that can allow the heart to be twisted into hate within any of the faiths based in love, peace, acceptance, and understanding. It is the reclusive hooligans and ne'er-do-wells who seemingly will lend themselves to any cause just for the sake of being able to commit acts of war, terror, or crimes against anyone as long as it provides them power, prestige, and even money. Usama, at the end of the Afghan war against the Soviets, wasn't willing to lay down his arms after the fight and sought a new enemy in order to maintain his control over his followers. Usama, and others like him, see themselves as the new prophet.

What of those without a declared religious belief? There are those who call themselves spiritual while avoiding any convictions to established faiths and religions. They are quasi-religious. They claim to be a step above an atheist but still very much worldly.

Marten often thought about how these misguided al Qaeda types, versus other mainstream Muslims, justified their actions based on the precepts of the religion they profess. Yet others state it is clearly not what Islam is and means. How they thought they would be meritorious to obtain this stature and unique place in God's grace. They would find the vision of heaven was just a chimera, just another canard perseverated by Usama and others to foment false hope and foment hate of those "others" who are different. He holds out the notion of seventy-two virgins as some form of pornographic dream gone haywire. That they would indeed be surrounded by such beauty if they were martyred, but this heaven would become their hell as they would have these women eternally dancing around them while their hands and feet bound. Their eyes would be perpetually held open as punishment, not a reward, for all their untoward deportment in life.

The pull was so much that even amongst the GIJIAS there was jockeying. They vied for credit one minute after a successful event, casting aspersions upon other supposed Islamic-fundamentalist groups if they did not live up to their set of ununiform standards of their supposedly same faith. They deflected when it was convenient.

Some latter GIJIA groups pinned events upon al Qaeda to discredit it, to claim its own moral superiority. Its own presence as heir apparent to the now failing, flailing, and clear delegation to also-ran legatees to the true leaders of this Islamic fundamentalist's movement toward a new Islamic caliphate. That many would challenge authority is clear contention they are all about themselves, not their faith they profess.

It is that same misdirection and diversion tactics they used to gain and maintain a base of followers by disaffecting them from the allegiance of their traditional faith principles, which would sidetrack them from their hatred needed in order to attack. The military had always used diversions and misinformation to divide the enemy forces. The GIJIAS looked to make use of that approach for the battles of both weapons and minds.

Like the magician Marten ended up seeing while in Laughlin, the GIJIAS used sleight of hand and misdirection to deceive Western forces. They tried to misdirect attention while manipulating things with the other hand.

Recent increased chatter over the previous ninety days had been overwhelming. Everything from post offices to local eateries in cities across the United States were being mentioned directly by name. Almost all conceivable methods of attack from homemade fertilizer bombs to out-right assaults with AK-47s that had gone missing from LA's docks way back in January 2006, to small plane hijacking threats were being discussed. If it was built to drive or fly, it was bound to have been mentioned. Planes, trains, and automobiles were promised to be used in a nationwide strike to mark a non-specific Muslim commemoration date.

The "day of atonement" was referenced and was hinted at being anything from a traditional Islamic holy day to the anniversary of any and every confirmed, and even remotely suggested, terrorist attack by Middle East jihadist organizations. Afghanistan, Iran, Iraq, Syria, and a dozen more Middle East and Islamic African states had been implicated.

"All quiet on the Northern front" was all that a recent coded message read. Was that a signal to launch attacks? Was that enough to foretell that something was indeed afoot? Should the threat level be raised, even though reportage of its still being a measurement maintained in DC nonexistent, and in just what target sectors? The Homeland Security Director and top aides were pouring over the entire previous months and the latest of intelligence of all known terrorist active cells trying to discern just that.

Somewhere in all the potential disinformation, and possible attempts at misdirection, had to be a shred of truth. Somehow, it was theorized, that a new coding was being employed by flooding the airwaves with threats in the codes that every government on the face of the earth had cracked. Somewhere in this madness there must be some rhyme and reason to those who knew what they were looking for. There was speculation that the complete opposite was also true, that perhaps there was no pattern, that the flood of information was just that. A message to go with whatever you've got. Hit the US or one of its allies now, or just mindless misdirection chatter to make Western agencies run around like Chickens with their heads cut off?

17

NAPERVILLE

I THINK THAT'S HOW CHICAGO GOT STARTED.
A BUNCH OF PEOPLE IN NEW YORK SAID,
"GEE, I'M ENJOYING THE CRIME AND THE POVERTY,
BUT IT JUST ISN'T COLD ENOUGH. LET'S GO WEST."

—Richard Jeni

*C*ammie merrily skipped and hopped around the lobby of the Naperville station as her mother Theresa attentively watched for the safety and well-being of her child. Cammie was excited. This was to be her first train ride. Plus, she was enthusiastic to be on their way to see auntie Carrie in the outer area of the sprawling Chicago area.

Cammie was full of energy. Hyped up on having had a vanilla shake along with her pancakes smothered in sugary maple syrup as part of her lunner! Yes, lunner. It was like brunch combines breakfast and lunch—brunch being that in between time. Lunner was eaten around 3:00 p.m. and combined lunch and dinner. Cammie calls it linner not quite getting the direct comparable term it should have the first-two letters of the first term of the combination like brunch. Theresa hoped she'd burn off at least some of her vigor before time to board the east-bound train, though there would indeed be a good degree of running up and down the aisle of the passenger car still too.

Theresa scanned away from monitoring Cammie for a moment to examine the ever-crowding waiting area. Early Friday afternoons are heavy travel times for those who could get out of work to get a jump on the weekend. Driving was certainly an option, but the freeways would already be packed and getting worse. Besides Theresa's sister Carrie could easily pick them up from the station near her; herself being able to avoid majority of the over-crowded main roadways.

This visit was Christmas in July type event this trip out, as Carrie had Christmas gifts that Cammie hadn't received yet still sitting in her closet. Months after the holidays, but months still before Cammie's birthday; and more gifts from Carrie. Those would be sent through the United States Postal Service package delivery system in order she would have those in time for her blowing out the candles tradition.

Theresa had to admonish Cammie for her squealing that filled the room. No one could hear the station clerk who came out from behind his barred window to make an announcement about the coming train. It could easily be understood that most of the room tacitly comprehended the point, as they were looking down at their watches to check the time.

"Please do not bother that nice man," Theresa said, again trying to reign Cammie in, this time from directly disrupting a gentleman from likely doing some work as he shuffled through papers. The young stranger had temporarily seated herself next to him and began telling him the story of her and mommies outing.

"It's fine. She's okay," the businessman said politely. "I do not yet have children. I do not mind her enthusiasm and desire to share."

By that time, it was too late. The little bundle of get-up-and-go had already shifted and got up and went to gleefully, mindlessly bouncing about the place again. Theresa thought to herself that those with children knew that trying to keep the child seated and quiet here, would result in rambunctiousness later. It was an attempt to not make her pay now, or we'd all pay later mindset. Better to let her loose a bit in this more open space, than the confines of the train car. Cammie would be ten times more fidgety on the train if not allowed to burn up some of the verve now. She also thought, as adults often do, if only us adults could have just a portion of that dynamism still.

Theresa thought twice about inviting Cammie over to sit down to perhaps read her book, basically the *Frozen* movie transcribed to text and some imagery from the cartoon. This and another book were hopeful distractions that might keep Cammie in her seat on the train for at least a portion of the twenty-five or so minutes in transit. Certainly, it was a relief they would avoid the additional ten-minute stretch into Chicago's Union Station and then the added hustle and bustle and elbow-to-elbow crowds.

"I'm thirsty," Cammie announced now directly in front of Theresa.

She, of course, wanted another sugary drink, but Theresa gave her a bottle of flavored water instead. Introducing yet more sugar would be bad parenting move in her mind. Theresa always attempted a degree of balance, giving Cammie some slack at times not wanting to be an overboard and overbearing overly strict helicopter mom. Raising Cammie, the way Theresa herself was raised the intention, no parenting books required.

"Just a few sips, and then we need to visit the bathroom as the train will be here soon." That piqued Cammie's excitement once again. She proceeded to get water on her face and the floor by trying to drink it while alternating from feet flat on the ground to tippy toed like a ballerina position, multiple times.

Rather than get upset, Theresa produced some facial tissue from her pocket to wipe the floor. All part of the process of any kids' day. From spurts of "holy terror" rants and motions, at least in the old-school phrase, the modern era now avoids in relation to children, to times of needing a nap. Even keel days, where they act more like a human than a Tasmanian devil, were few and far between. Then they were off to the potty. Thankfully, no issues, as this station had a nice, separate "family use" bathroom.

The train was pulling into the station while they were exiting the lavatory, so there would be no more pestering everyone in the lobby. That would now be solely reserved for the lucky folks sitting in the same rail car. Theresa took Cammie's left hand, clinging to their shared laptop bag-turned miniature suitcase, and they shuffled with the others toward the awaiting tracked vehicle.

Cammie was old enough, and quick-witted enough, to let out a "moo" as the procession moved along. Theresa would have laughed but knew it would only then encourage a "baa" sound next. Instead, she thought to change the subject.

"Look, you can see the front of the train," she said pointing to the right. "Sometimes rather than locomotive they call that a battleship, which is where the engineer drives the train from," Theresa explained.

"See the back of the train?" not waiting for response; knowing Cammie knew, from the board-game, that a battleship goes through the water and may want to know why a train would be called that, and Theresa, not having the answer, quickly continued, "That is the caboose," motioning to the left now, "in the movies they sometimes call that the clown car."

That did the trick as Cammie quizzically pondered aloud, "I wonder why they call it that?"

And with that Cammie was enthralled with taking in all else in relation to their transport method. They entered their car, found their seats, and awaited to get underway. They were both barely nestled into their seats when Cammie decided she had to know where the others were going. Perhaps they might be going to meet their aunty too? As Cammie approached the front of the car, she saw a man in his early twenties, clearly, in Cammie's mind, must've innocently forgot his backpack and was exiting the train. "Mommy, that man forgot his backpack. Can I go tell him?"

Theresa innocently thought little about it, but before she could respond another passenger jumped up and shouted for Cammie to get away from the luggage. The conductor, who had just entered the car, was verbally accosted by the now hysterical traveler, who began to scream at him about suspicious package protocol. The conductor quickly looked around and low and behold there was indeed an unattended backpack.

"To whom does this belong?" he bellowed, pointing to the bag on a seat in the front row while slowly backing away.

"The man that just got off the train," Cammie said, trying to explain. Others roared above her with their proclamations of not knowing and other muddled remarks. Cammie tugged at the conductor's pant leg as he'd now moved closer to her retreat toward Theresa nearer the rear.

"Everyone off the train," he hollered and then spoke into his walkie-talkie. "Unattended package. Car three. Over."

The conductor realized his bad reaction. Instead, he needed to clear the train in a calm, at least outward appearance thereof, fashion. People harming themselves in a chaotic stampede from the cars would create potentially greater issues of then injured needing savior on the train with the package by means of the then only a potentially unknown danger.

"Please, calmly, and in an orderly fashion, exit the train," he now offered in a still forceful tone but more controlled manner.

The hysterical rider was clearly panicked, and hurriedly rushed from his seat and past others now standing in the aisleway. Slowly they all began their trek toward the rear exit. Fortunately, no one was hurt in his zeal, but he had no problem pushing people out of his way in his hasty unplanned exit. Other station attendants had boarded the train and was evacuating the other cars similarly.

The ticket-taker having heard the Conductor's walkie-talkie warning had notified Naperville city authorities, but it would take them a few minutes to respond. So, he was on the platform directing traffic. As people stepped down, he shouted over the din of concerned chatter for people to work their way to the front of the station house for protection. He made clear to not loiter in the lobby waiting area. While he didn't fully articulate his statement was clearly indicating people should shield using the building. Distance themselves from any potential hazard, still to be determined existed or not.

The man Cammie had seen leave the bag was now long into the wind. Who was he? What might he have been doing on the train? And why would he be leaving behind his bag? Security footage may have picked up a motor vehicle he was leaving the scene in, to help track him down, but that was currently a secondary thought at this moment. Getting the customers and employees safely away of any potential risk was first and foremost the priority.

They'd studied all the manuals. They've had meetings on the protocols. This, however, was 'real world' and not speculation nor an exercise. The real deal. Lives could hang in the balance. While anxious, the need to appear calm and reassuring was a must.

Seconds seemed like minutes. Minutes dragged on. A Naperville police officer finally ran up the platform from his car he left abandoned in the drive along the station. Hopefully, while we may all need a Saviour, hopefully no-one would really be in need of a first-responder savior today.

Soon thereafter, Naperville fire respondents arrived with medical assistants in tow. After a quick assessment of the situation, they knew there was no time to waste and made a call for help from Chicago's bomb squad and requested that the FBI be notified.

Everyone was now safely distanced from the threat, and no explosives detonated, as the protocol called to safeguard against occurring. Yet! Now all they could do was wait for the bomb squad to arrive and cautiously approach the knapsack to do their thing to analyze the threat, as to being whether reality or fiction.

Theresa held Cammie tight to her person. Additional police had arrived, blocking the parking lot. No one was going to be going anywhere soon. The police began inquiring about everyone's well-being and taking statements as the drama on the other side of the building continued to unfold.

The hysterical passenger, now calmer, and that seemed to know the most about necessary procedures, was talking to a small conglomeration of folks huddled around him. He was explaining that if it was indeed something other than mere absent-mindedness, an honest mistake, maybe it could be similar to the Atlanta Olympics bomber situation: an abandoned backpack with ill-intent, to hurt, maim, potentially kill all in the vicinity. He offered a prayer of thanks to God that it hadn't detonated while they were still huddled in the railcar, and would've then turned potential death-trap.

It finally sunk in. Theresa realized they may have indeed narrowly escaped death. She always chose to think positively. She treated others decently and expected them to be decent toward her, so the events unfolding was indeed a very rude shock to her system. Theresa also finally came to the realization that Cammie was likely the only one who paid any notice to the owner of that backpack. The police would need to know this as soon as possible. She released her clutch on Cammie, who was understandably in a confused state, and told her, "We need to tell a nice policeman what you saw on the train." Cammie nodded her head, and they made their way to the nearest uniformed first responder.

Before they could reach one of the "protectors of the peace" as Cammie was taught, someone cried out, "Get down! Please crouch down!" Someone had spotted through the railcar window some smoke. It was a faint but rising from the seat on which the luggage had been abandoned. It was now clear something more than just books were in that bag. There was a smoldering.

After a few minutes, a police captain arrived and took command of the scene – at least until the FBI arrived, as it was looking more and more like a terrorism site. It now was time to move folks from the building. He radioed instruction to those under his command to move the people further back to the far side of the parking lot for questioning.

Fortunately, no one was injured. As the day turned to night, they were all interviewed, and it was determined it was undeniably an IED that failed to detonate as planned and which the bomb squad had safely disarmed and removed from the train.

Those that now wished to reboard could, belatedly, be on their way to other stations. The train authorities were glad there were no injuries that day, but they still had a mess on their hands. Trains were now backed up on tracks or at stations for miles in all directions. This would take several more hours, if not all night, to clean up. Not to mention people were worried that another device could exist on another train. Another would-be assassin potentially then awaiting detonation of a device once they've exited. It was, only clear, to this point, there were no murder-suicide bombers this day. No-one willing to detonate a device while still in their possession.

Theresa, now sufficiently jolted to the terrorism reality hoisted upon her, decided a trip to Carrie's would have to wait another day. The only trip happening now was back to the perceived safety, and if nothing else comfort, of their apartment building. It was far more excitement Cammie would likely be able to handle for one day.

Tomorrow would be the day to investigate a refund or ticket exchange for a potential future travel date. She would spend the remainder of the night cuddling with Cammie, filling in the blanks to questions she would undoubtedly have about the event, getting her to bed early, hopefully Cammie would be worn out from the excitement and quick to sleep. Theresa had already spoken with Carrie, during some of the idle time in the parking lot, to explain why she never received a call of their arrival and the uncertainty she was a part of and would call her again to discuss more in-depth once Cammie was slumbering.

Even though such a terrorist attack attempt might be deemed a failure by some, it has succeeded. Even when they don't kill countless people, the terror will reverberate for days, weeks, and months in the lives of those involved in the close call. It would change the lives of those directly involved forever.

Those wishing to sow discord, confusion, and terror need not cause mass fatalities to effectively cause an ongoing panic amid the masses. Just the knowledge that those wanting us dead have not ceased operations is sufficient. They have tried before and will try again, and again and again and again. A fanatical enemy can be stopped only one way. It's either us or them. We thwart and lock them up or end them before they end us.

Theresa never before wished anyone harm. Though she was not a religious person per se herself, she always wanted blessings and a good life to be bestowed upon others. She certainly never desired for anyone to die, outside the assuredness of an inevitable natural causes, but the realities of the cold, hard veracity, of the here and now; and, yes, sure, crime certainly claimed the lives prematurely of far too many, but this is a far more hideous and pure-evil sense to it came crashing into her own backyard that day. When enemies of the coexistence mentality demonstrate, they are committed to fight to the death, then they must be obliged for the greater good, peace, and security, of those who wish to live in harmony.

Theresa, while she thought she was fully mindful of the need to be a protector of her child, realized she was far more an ostrich on this topic than the mama bear she needed to be.

Just how close to death were they, should the IED have exploded? She wasn't sure, but it was a massive awakening.

18

TERROR STRIKES – NEW YORK

IT'S THE WIND UP. THE PITCH.
HE GOT A LOT OF MUSTARD ON THAT ONE.

*I*t had been a long summer, finally a chance at attending a baseball game before it would near the end of the season arrived.

Zeeiod told his son Larry to hurry up or they would be late for the baseball game. His full name was Lawrence, but only his mom called him that when she was letting him know he'd be in trouble when dad got home. Zeeiod, being of Arab descent, named him for his love of Peter O'Toole's *Lawrence of Arabia*. Zeeiod named his first child, Lawrence's older sister, Lauren, the female equivalent. Lawrence felt cheated as there was basically no difference in their names. He was upset as a younger brother against an elder sibling often is for no good reason. Big sis got the derivation. He would have preferred something dissimilar to hers. Perhaps something more Americana. He would have preferred Rob after Rob O'Neill the SEa, Air, and Land force, more commonly referred to as SEAL, Team Six member who ultimately shot Usama bin Laden in the raid in Pakistan trying to apprehend the ten-million-dollar FBI wanted bounty terrorist. There would be no uncertainty where young Lawrence's allegiances lay.

Lawrence was very much the average American kid. He loved hot dogs, baseball, apple pie, and Chevrolet as the old commercial goes. He was not born until many years those advertisements were gone from the TV airwaves, and even long after 9/11, but he had seen President Bush throw out the first pitch of Game 3 of the World Series between the New York Yankees and the Arizona Diamondbacks on October 30, 2001.

There had been a spattering of sporting events that took place in the immediate aftermath of 9/11, but the eyes of the nation were on Bush junior, or "W" as he is most notably referred, and his first-pitch. That day was important, it was special, as though the entire nation breathed a collective sigh of relief when he winged his pitch over the plate from atop the mound.

It provided some semblance of normalcy for all the places not still in and directly around Ground Zero and the Pentagon – Shanksville, Pennsylvania, with no real damage to the area an afterthought. It was a signal that the United States had taken the necessary steps to ensure domestic tranquility going forward, at least from any other potential major follow-up attacks in the immediate future.

Baseball ran deep in Lawrence's red-blooded American veins. Any chance at a trip to a baseball game, even minor-leaguers, was welcomed. He had been looking forward to this day since he put it on the calendar when Zeeiod informed him he had purchased the tickets for the Saturday night contest two weeks prior.

Lawrence ran out of his room that is adorned with many a New York Yankees paraphernalia. He wanted to be emersed in it. He thought he would either be a professional baseball player; hopefully on his way to the majors and to play for the Yanks, or become a Navy SEAL like his idol O'Neill.

Lawrence announced his concern, "Where's my glove?"

"You put it in the car last night already," Zeeiod informed him.

With that, they were out the front door and on their way to the ballpark. Apparently, Lawrence wasn't the only one that had the date circled on the calendar though. Across town diabolical plans were being set into motion. Two cold-blooded murderers from abroad, having been in the United States for many years, were well aware of the Americana nature and its people's love of baseball. They too seen rerun after rerun of the Bush pitch. To them, if baseball signaled some return to normalcy, they would use it to disrupt normal on a grand scale.

They reveled in the thought of hitting those damn Yankees as slur for all Americans, not the baseball team, but was indeed one more direct connection of New York being the New York Yankee's home-state. Though the cry "Damn Yankees" had been heard around the world in modern times, it was used even back during the United States Civil War. It really originated long before that when Dutch residents used it as a term for settlers to Connecticut. How it then all became twisted from there is unknown.

New York must be the place for the attack, for all the potential connected reasonings. It was the home of baseball's best known and always a premier team, the Bush pitch, Wall-Street, and more. It would be like pouring salt in 9/11 wounds still unhealed among so many. It clearly could not be NYC itself, but New York State would certainly suffice. They made a martyr recording laying out their motives plain. Should they die in the incursion, authorities would recover it from their premises. Like others before them, though, they had no plans on murder-suicide rather they preferred a hit-and-run attack so as to live to attack another day. They hoped to have a series of hits at not just baseball, but other sporting events. New American football leagues were forming, and would provide very tempting targets at, maybe some smaller stadiums, softer targets with easier access, likely less extensive security measures based upon smaller budgets, than the big-brother football league.

Their plan was a copycat attack, a combination of Oklahoma City fertilizer bombing via U-Haul truck and the Tokyo subway poison. The rental truck, acquired under fake identification, was packed with fertilizer, ignitors, and crude toxins. It was all rigged to be detonated from a burner phone. They had learned the skills from terror cells training camps in Afghanistan, Somalia, and Syrian hot zones.

The back was sealed, and they too were on their way toward the stadium. They were not privy to Marten and his book, but they too thought of the duality of certain terms beyond the tacit ties to America's game, the George Bush insult they felt but that too of a "strike" at a game that used balls and strikes as part of its nomenclature. The connection provided a chance to laugh in the face at those they killed. Their personal inside joke, regardless of their success would be sure to be examined for years to come.

Marten and them, worlds apart; culturally, religiously, and politically; yet having a similar thought about word play among certain terms and the added potential psychological extent that it might achieve beyond that of its introduction. Marten, hoping for it to apply for good with the interplay of the "tracks" term; a sense of connection for vigilance; but for the terrorists a bit of a rubbing-it-in-the-wound and additional terror that American complacency again wrought using the "strikes" interplay. Bonus, it was thought, the very team names involved.

Marten had flown into New York direct from Detroit, and Nic from Vegas, for another meetup to discuss aspects of Marten's book. They were carpooling to Ambassador Stadium thirty miles outside NYC with tickets for the evening competition between the New Yorkers and the Americans baseball clubs.

It was a convergence of his book efforts and an active, unbeknownst to them, in-process live attack. Nic brought some more notes, things he would not want transmitted in electronic form in any way to his friend, and he wanted to read the portions of Marten's transcript to date during an overnight stay in NYC.

A trip to the 9/11 Memorial and Ground Zero were to provide some direct stimuli for Marten. Something to reaffirm his motivations. It would provide food for thought, additional inspiration, and a somber time to reflect upon all those lost – and even all those still suffering both physical and mental scars. He hoped to listen in on the chatter of those around the memorial as they discussed what was on their minds, all these years later, about that fateful day in September 2001, as Marten and Nic walked through. He anticipated some anger would creep in during the visit as he reflected on all those who have now seemingly forgot. Yes, after all these years many have forgotten the pains and emotions of that day, many of whom previously had pledged to never forget!

Nic was driving so Marten could pound the pen to his yellow legal pad after leaving the area and their visit to the 9/11 Memorial Museum with its forty thousand plus images from the fateful day and the aftermath. There were multiple thousands of audio recordings directly related to the attacks, a few-hundred hours of video, and more artifacts related than all the images and recordings combined. They spent time around the reflecting pool and the list of names that now outlined the former footprint of the Twin Towers as they were most often referred as.

They visited all the immediate area now themed, to correspond with the new travel industry of 9/11 tourism, though Marten hated that word, and the additionally inspired new architecture. *Themed*, Marten thought was far too happy and festive a word, though he wasn't sure yet what he would convert that to within the pages of his book. The word *themed* made him think of an amusement park. It bothered him the same way calling 9/11 an anniversary did. Clearly that was another word intended for happy things like wedding anniversaries, and the like. September 11 was a somber commemorative REMEMBRANCE DAY!

Before heading on toward Ambassador Field they made a detour to the Washingtonville first responders memorial specifically dedicated to five firefighters who died in the 9/11 terror strikes. They wanted to see the improvements made after the small area of the park in which it was placed, they heard was vandalized in 2020. The flagpole, with its flag at half-staff, was toppled. Graffiti defaced other aspects of the tribute.

Soon, the clash of these peoples, Zeeiod, Lawrence, Marten, Nicolas, others, and the terrorists, very contradicting purposes would meet. A convergence of cultures, goals, pursuits, and all their lives to be forever more and inexplicably altered.

Zeeiod and Lawrence had arrived and were engaging in idle chit-chat and exchanging pleasantries as one does with somewhat frequently encountered acquaintances, with so many of the security, ticket-takers, and the like, they'd come to know over the years as they made their way along. They looked forward to a day of fun. These were not mere workers but were considered more than even only mere acquaintances but indeed friends, albeit not close as their only contact was at these gatherings. They considered them friends nonetheless, people whom they've come to know and care about.

Marten, Nic, and so many others joined them in the comingling near the entrance gates. Marten coincidentally struck up a conversation with Lawrence about his bringing his glove to the game with, no doubt in Marten's mind, hopes that Lawrence would manage to be able to catch a foul ball, or at least scoop up a practice ball hit down the left field line where they were to sit.

They paid little attention to the truck that pulled in behind the TV crew van that would be uploading the game broadcast. Nor did the truck capture the attention of the Ambassador Stadium security crew busy scrutinizing the crowds forming before them; any more than the two men dressed in overalls hoping to be confused for ordinary maintenance crew would attract if they indeed pulled off their guise getting out of it.

Lawrence only started to respond to this stranger's inquiry when the blast shattered the atmosphere of amusement and indulgence.

The perpetrators looked back upon their work as they walked away; it had not gone to plan. They had expected a much greater blast radius. However, not to worry they thought. Regardless of whatever damage the explosion failed to do to the exterior of the stadium and harming patrons, the expanding toxic gas it was also meant to propel would affect those downed by the discharge of shrapnel. They hoped to also infect those would be savior first responders to the initial marks.

Lawrence was down and writhing in pain. He had been struck by debris. Nic had quickly pounced to his feet. His training kicked in. He first checked Marten, who had been struck. Blood streamed from his left leg, but Marten was more concerned about others potentially in poorer condition. He motioned Nic toward Lawrence.

Nic ripped off his shirt to create tourniquets for the wounded in his immediate vicinity when the pungent smell became apparent. This was clearly not just a burn smell from the blast. Nic feared it was something much more dangerous. The odor became more prominent and everyone's breathing become labored. Security personnel that were nearby, having shifted their focus from the front gate and to those nearby, began to fall to their knees effected by the toxins. Grasping for air, their potential fate raced in their minds supplanting the pains knowing that fire and other rescue personnel were still a good amount of time away. Were any security personnel even in sufficient shape to converse over communication devices to warn of the additional present dangers? Others would come and would be overtaken.

In just a short time, it was uncertain as to whether they too may pass and become another statistic of terror casualties.

Appendix A
BEHIND THE BOOK

*I*f you've read the book, you'll know most of this, and I certainly hope you enjoyed the read and will recommend to others. There will be some additional insight you may wish to glean from this section. However, in addition, we know that some will peek at the back first before purchase (if that is you, you've just been "busted cheating" but by all means please keep reading this closing section for some insight about the book).

The central character in this book has built his life around the written word. Through this character's wealth of knowledge, contacts, and expertise, we reviewed factual based information and provided historical perspective to the fictional story.

By employing a book within a book and blog within a book format, I tried to give a balance between providing information that you may, or may not, already be aware and neatly placing it in a format that stood out from the storyline.

Most will be familiar with, at least, the headlines that were generated as result of the terrorist activities outlined within the pages of this manuscript. Time, however, has shed additional light and information on those events and the news. In other cases, what appeared to be clear has been clouded by new information than what you may have known or thought at the time.

The use of factual information and real individuals intertwined with fictional characters and events allows for the reader to connect with enhanced realism. The global implication of the terrorist communities and impact throughout the world. Inside was past terrorist targets, both those that were successfully translated into terrorist attacks, some that were thwarted, and those that have been hypothesized.

I tried to use this media to impart some basic knowledge, wisdom, concepts, theories in an attempt to provide more than just a basic work of fiction. The desire is to provide the readers mind with food for thought in the realms of psychology, theism, and politics.

You decide whether or not to follow up on the introduction of these concepts. The political points are suited for discussion around your water-cooler or political party rally.

Joseph M. Lenard

As stated above, time has shed light on things past, as they will going forward, so be aware that more updates, added information, and supplemental links, will be maintained at https://TerrorStrikes.info/introduction and https://TerrorStrikes.info/links, post publication of this book you may wish to review from time to time.

Appendix B
REWARDS

JEHAD SERWAN MOSTAFA

Conspiracy to Provide Material Support to Terrorists; Conspiracy to Provide Material Support to a Foreign Terrorist Organization; Providing Material Support to a Foreign Terrorist Organization

The United States government is offering a reward of up to $5 million for information leading directly to the apprehension or conviction of Jehad Serwan Mostafa.

https://www.fbi.gov/wanted/wanted_terrorists/jehad-serwan-mostafa

Reward exists for the above identified Person(s) as well as other individuals in response for expected Terrorist activities against the United States and other sovereign governments. Contact the United States (FBI) Federal Bureau of Investigation, U.S. Consulate, or U.S. Embassy.

If you have any information concerning this person, please contact your local FBI office or use http://www.fbi.gov/contact-us/ form or contact American Embassy or Consulate. You may also call 1-800-CALL-FBI (1-800-225-5324), or submit tips online at https://tips.fbi.gov/.

MOHAMMED ALI HAMADEI

Conspiracy to Commit Aircraft Piracy, to Commit Hostage Taking, to Commit Air Piracy Resulting in Murder, to Interfere With a Flight Crew, to Place a Destructive Device Aboard an Aircraft, to Have Explosive Devices About the Person on an Aircraft, and to Assault Passengers and Crew; Air Piracy Resulting in Murder; Air Piracy; Hostage Taking; Interference With Flight Crew; and Placing Explosives Aboard Aircraft; Placing Destructive Devices Aboard Aircraft; Assault Aboard Aircraft With Intent to Hijack With a Dangerous Weapon and Resulting in Serious Bodily Injury; Aiding and Abetting

The United States Government is offering a reward of up to $5 million for information leading directly to the apprehension or conviction of Mohammed Ali Hamadei.

https://www.fbi.gov/wanted/wanted_terrorists/mohammed-ali-hamadei

Reward exists for the above identified Person(s) as well as other individuals in response for expected terrorist activities against the United States and other sovereign governments. Contact the United States (FBI) Federal Bureau of Investigation, U.S. Consulate, or U.S. Embassy.

You may also call 1-800-CALL-FBI (1-800-225-5324), or submit tips online at https://tips.fbi.gov/.

AHLAM AHMAD Al TAMIMI

Conspiring to Use and Using a Weapon of Mass Destruction Against a United States National Outside the United States Resulting in Death and Aiding and Abetting and Causing an Act to be Done

The United States Government is offering a reward of up to $5 million for information leading directly to the apprehension or conviction of Ahlam Ahmad al Tamimi.

https://www.fbi.gov/wanted/wanted_terrorists/ahlam-ahmad-al-tamimi

Reward exists for the above identified Person(s) as well as other individuals in response for expected Terrorist activities against the United States and other sovereign governments. Contact the United States (FBI) Federal Bureau of Investigation, U.S. Consulate, or U.S. Embassy.

You may also call 1-800-CALL-FBI (1-800-225-5324), or submit tips online at https://tips.fbi.gov/.

JOANNE DEBORAH CHESIMARD

Act of Terrorism - Domestic Terrorism; Unlawful Flight to Avoid Confinement – Murder

The United States Government is offering a reward of up to $1 million for information leading directly to the apprehension or conviction of Joanne Deborah Chesimard.

https://www.fbi.gov/wanted/wanted_terrorists/joanne-deborah-chesimard

Reward exists for the above identified Person(s) as well as other individuals in response for expected Terrorist activities against the United States and other sovereign governments. Contact the United States (FBI) Federal Bureau of Investigation, U.S. Consulate, or U.S. Embassy.

You may also call 1-800-CALL-FBI (1-800-225-5324), or submit tips online at https://tips.fbi.gov/.

More: https://www.fbi.gov/wanted/wanted_terrorists

CPSIA information can be obtained
at www.ICGtesting.com
Printed in the USA
JSHW022242270522
26334JS00002B/180